Trauma to Triumph

Stories of TBI Survivors
and the Vital Role of Post-Acute Care

Contributing Authors:
Patricia Donini, James B. Durham III,
Laurie Elinoff, Grace W. Bureau Elsner,
David A. Grant, Susan M. Hahn,
Doug Hoffman, Meighen Lovelace,
Darcy L. Keith, Pasha Palanker, Dina Potter,
Lori Raggio, Carrie E. Rickert,
Debra Baker Scheinberg, Evan Scheinberg,
and Kristie Warren

Edited by Elizabeth B. Hill, MSW,
and Mary Ann Pack

Green Heart Living Press

Trauma to Triumph: Stories of TBI Survivors and the Vital Role of Post Acute Care

Copyright © 2022

ISBN (paperback): 978-1-954493-24-7

Cover artwork and design: Barb Pritchard and Elizabeth Hill

Dedication

This book is dedicated to Karin Hahn
who was a true warrior during the final ten years of
her painful life. Karin's fight to live is what gave her
sister Susan the inspiration and determination to
launch a Foundation dedicated to helping others.

Dear Deb,

Yes, this is a second book with your name on it. Susan told me a close friend of Dave's experienced a TBI. This book is for Dave's friend, if you/Dave want to pass it on to him. I'm sorry I don't even know his name. Any friend of yours is part of my extended family.

Enjoy,

Susan

Table of Contents

Dear Reader,

your path may feel uncertain

the path may seem dark, too complicated, impossible

you are on a path that is just your path

a path no one has walked before

but many have found themselves in this same place

it has felt dark, too complicated, impossible

on these pages, our authors put words to the indescribable

they share what helped them create a new life

from a very uncertain place

you have your own path to walk

but we've seen places like this

you are not alone

we can walk the path with you

Love & Courage,

Elizabeth

Introduction

"When you're surrounded by people who share a passionate commitment around a common purpose, anything is possible."
Howard Schultz

Well before sustaining a traumatic brain injury (TBI) in 2013, I had become fascinated by scientific studies about how the brain works. My initial work and learning about neuroscience began in 2006 when I did some work for David Rock, author of *Quiet Leadership, Coaching with the Brain in Mind, Your Brain at Work*, and other books. This is when I first heard the term neuroplasticity. As John Ratey, clinical professor of psychiatry at Harvard Medical School is quoted in *Quiet Leadership*, "There are more possible ways to connect the brain's neurons than there are atoms in the universe." Each of our brains has up to 100 billion neurons, and our brains are connecting the neurons in new ways every single day. In my chapter, I share the remarkable empirical validation that if one part of a brain is damaged, another part can assume the role of the damaged part.

As much as I love learning and talking about the brain, my intention now is to share some of the themes culled from the chapters in this book. There are no two brains on this planet that are identical. Thus, there are no two TBIs that are identical. What I found of great interest is the number of times similar words and phrases appeared in the chapters, relating both to the disabling aspects, and the beliefs that supported recovery. The following are some of the themes.

Disabling Aspects of TBIs

<u>Memory</u> - Memory loss tends to be the most common consequence of a TBI. It is typically short-term, though long-term memory can suffer as well. The short-term memory challenge can cause the survivor to repeat the same thing multiple times. In some cases, family members and others communicating with a TBI survivor repeating themselves will assume the onset of dementia. Most every author shares their experience of memory loss. At five years post-accident, I participated in eight hours of neuropsychiatric testing to rule out early signs of dementia.

<u>Headaches</u> - An increase in headaches is common. For some, the headaches mirror what are known as migraine headaches, with symptoms including extreme sensitivity to light, vertigo, nausea, impact on eyesight, etc. Again, not every headache is the same as another.

<u>Isolation</u> - As you will read in these chapters, there are many reasons survivors end up feeling isolated. Sometimes this means being physically

alone, typically leading to emotional pain. In other cases, the survivor may live with and interact with others, while feeling isolated from reality.

Depression - Episodes of depression go hand-in-hand with TBIs, some symptoms more serious than others. The authors share various descriptions of what led them into depression. Examples include feeling hopeless, helpless, destined to fail, alienated, vulnerable, disabled for life, etc.

Hiding - You will read how the word invisible is used in these chapters; invisible wound, invisible disability, invisible injury. We may use different words, but the sentiment is the same. With a cast on an arm or leg, or the use of a wheelchair or crutches, those around you know there is some level of limitation or disability. You can't look at a TBI survivor and see the brain injury, and most survivors don't want to disclose they suffered an injury to their brain. As a result, many survivors go to extreme lengths to hide their disability. I can attest to the fact that trying to mask or hide the injury can be exhausting.

Brain Fatigue - I have not met another survivor who did not experience brain fatigue. Unless you have experienced a TBI, I'm not sure most people can relate to it, and it's difficult to explain.

Beliefs that Result in Healing

There are equally as many, if not more, beliefs that create the strength to keep moving forward. Some of the themes are described below.

Faith - The most frequently referenced belief revolved around faith, primarily faith in God, though also faith in themselves, in their family, and in other caregivers or loved ones.

Hard Work - For many, once it becomes clear that no one is going to wave a wand or give you a pill to heal your brain, working hard becomes part of a daily practice.

Movement - We have all heard how important it is to exercise. As some of the authors have experienced, if a muscle is not used, it will atrophy. In my case, my right leg was not exercised for more than six months, reducing the muscle mass by close to half the size of the left leg. The brain is also a muscle and will experience the same.

Purpose - Having a purpose, regardless of its nature, will increase the motivation needed to keep moving forward. The movement may begin with baby steps and that's okay. For certain personality types, such as what we know as Type A personalities, there may be frustration to overcome. These are the people who are accustomed to getting it done and getting it done fast. That does not work when recovering from a TBI. Keep the purpose in front of you and you'll get there. Within each of these chapters, you will learn more about purpose.

Patience - It takes time to heal. Depending on the severity of an injury, the healing process can continue for the rest of one's life. This goes for any injury. Give it time and be kind to yourself!

Many survivors talk about wanting to go back to being themselves again. I share with them the words on a sign I made for my office which reads, "Don't look in the rearview mirror because you are not going that way." There is no such thing as going back to who you were, brain injury or not. In these chapters, you will read about life-altering transformations, some of which bring to life what has become known as TBI growth.

Resources

94 Post-Acute Resources are listed in this book, resources we relied on to support our journeys to triumph. We represent a new family of individuals who transformed our traumatic experiences into support of TBI survivors headed to triumph.

> *"Nothing behind me, everything ahead of me,*
> *as is ever so on the road."*
> Jack Kerouac

Susan M. Hahn

Chapter 1

Crossing Over

Susan M. Hahn

October 14, 2013 was a beautiful fall day. Leaves had morphed into vibrant shades of color. As I sat on the deck having a cup of coffee, a gust of wind appeared, and it suddenly looked like it was snowing leaves. A sprinkle of color covered the ground. As I watched the leaves, a kayaker appeared in the background, moving his paddle through sparkling water in perfect tempo.

Perfect seemed to be the word of the day. Everything was perfect for me to get on my bike and continue training. The date of October 14 was almost six weeks to the day after having crossed over the finish line of my first ever triathlon. I had convinced myself to stay in good physical shape to complete another triathlon. This meant regular biking, running, and swimming. I jumped on the bike and headed to the Baltimore and Annapolis

Trail (B & A Trail). It is part of the East Coast Greenway and extends 24.7 miles. The eight-foot-wide paved surface is well-maintained and provides walkers, riders, runners, and bikers a perfect passageway with trees lining both sides.

My plan was to ride for 18 miles and then jog for a few more. Almost immediately, I realized the bike's odometer was not working. I knew precisely at what point I would reach nine miles and had no need to know my speed, so I decided to ride the 18 miles and then take the bike to the Bike Doctor, a bike store near my home.

I was proud to have completed the 18 miles and was ready to drop the bike off at the Bike Doctor. Given that my home was within walking distance from the store, the plan was to drop off the bike and walk or jog home. To go from the trail to the bike store I had to cross a six-lane highway separated by a large median strip of grass. I crossed over the first three lanes and was waiting on the median strip to cross over the next three lanes. As I stood there, a car pulled up and stopped in the lane closest to me, only a few yards away. The woman waved at me to cross in front of her. I shook my head and said out loud, "No, PLEASE, you go." She did not. She continued to wave her arm indicating she wanted me to pass in front of her. By this time several cars were stopped behind this woman's car. They all began to wave and blow horns. I continued to stand firm that I would not go and they needed to proceed.

The seconds clicked by and then the second lane of traffic slowed to a stop. Now there were two lanes of cars stopped; waiving at me and blowing their horns encouraging me to go across. I placed my hands in prayer form and said loudly, "No, PLEASE, you go!" Not one car budged. I finally surrendered and began to quickly walk my bike over the lanes. I chose the word "surrendered" intentionally, as that is exactly what it felt like. Typically, surrendering is the last thing I choose, regardless of the situation. I made the choice to surrender in order not to continue inconveniencing all the people in those cars. It was as if the moment called for me to surrender.

I quickly crossed over the first two lanes. The third lane was wide open, except for the car that was traveling over 50 miles an hour, did not see me, and hit me. I was thrown 30 feet and sustained multiple injuries, including compound fractures of my leg and arm, and torn ligaments and muscles all along the right side of my body. I also suffered a traumatic brain injury (TBI). The following is what was shared by a witness listed in the police report.

The witness, a woman, said there were cars stopped on the northbound and southbound lanes of the highway. At the same time, people from both sides got out of their cars and started walking toward me. They did not speak to each other as they formed a tight circle around me and started saying prayers. The woman told me she stepped inside the circle of people to kneel beside me and pray. She took my hand and held it, rubbing the top of it with her other hand as she prayed. She was certain she knew what inspired so many people to quietly approach me to pray. She was certain that "at the same time, each person got a message, and the message had come from God." Divine intervention?

During the time I was surrounded in a circle of prayer, several people from the Bike Doctor ran out to see what had happened and if they could help. It was Brad, the manager of the store, who saw that my helmet and bike still had the Iron Girl Triathlon Race number on them. He went back to his office and searched the list of everyone who had completed the 2013 Iron Girl Triathlon. He found my race number, full name, and my age. This is how the police learned who I was. The witnesses did not think I was alive and conveyed this to the police. By this time, people from the media were present and thus, it was reported on TV news and in print that 58-year-old Susan Hahn had been pronounced dead at the scene. Yes, I could very well have crossed over in the dying process. What they failed to report, because it was not yet known, was that I was alive and hospitalized at Shock Trauma in Baltimore, MD.

Susan Hahn (middle) with Jon Korin (left) President AAA Biking and Lifeline 200 Annual Bike Race and Rick Ruck (right), Owner of several Bike Doctors in the state of Maryland

I had been flown to Shock Trauma and admitted to the resuscitation unit. Upon verification that I was alive, surgery was scheduled immediately, in order for me to not lose my leg. First my life, then my leg, were saved by the outstanding work of the surgical teams at the University of Maryland Shock Trauma Center.

Following the surgeries, I was transferred to an acute rehabilitation hospital. I had a cast on my right leg, an external fixator on my right arm, a brace on my left arm, and staples from the top of my head to my neck. There were days when the pain and exhaustion were so intense that I wanted the nurses to let me stay in bed for the day. Then I would remember how many people were pulling for me, praying for me, and sending me healing energy.

I was determined to heal and knew this meant hard work. I needed to internalize the power of prayer, believe in myself, and work hard. That meant three hours of therapy six days a week while in the acute rehabilitation hospital.

The therapies were physical, occupational, and speech (for retraining of the brain). They were critical in the healing process, helping me walk again, use my arms more effectively, and begin the gradual process of relearning words and improving memory. I was then transferred from inpatient to outpatient therapy, which I had three times a week for three hours a day. During the initial stages of recovery, I received overwhelming support from my husband Tony, other family members, and friends.

As casts and braces were removed, my primary injury (TBI) became invisible. The mental anguish I continued to experience was not understood and therefore disregarded. When the deepest of

19

depressions emerged, I asked to be left alone for several months to heal from the depression. This was the very last thing I needed but did not know any better. The consequence was feeling abandoned. I allowed myself, or really pushed myself, into complete isolation. Everyone in my life knew me as self-driven and in control. As a result, my wishes were honored and granted.

At discharge from outpatient therapy, I was not informed of additional post-acute treatment options to further improve my brain function. As with physical and occupational therapy, once the speech therapist deemed my brain and speech were functioning at the greatest level possible from therapy, I was discharged. I walked out of my final outpatient therapies in agony. I knew I was nowhere close to full TBI recovery.

After 15 months of speech therapy for my brain, all I could keep asking was, "Now What???!!!!" Part of the answer to the "what" was for me to build my own recovery plan. I knew long-term lack of muscle exercise results in atrophy. The same is true of the brain. If it is not worked, the function will continue to decline.

A key factor in my cognitive healing was believing and relying on how amazing our brains are at creating new connections, with endless adaptation abilities. During the first many months post-hospitalization, the external fixator rendered my right arm immobile, which forced me to either not write or learn to write with my left hand. Having studied neuroscience during my executive and physician leadership coach training, I knew about our brain's neuroplasticity. Even at 60 years old the brain can transfer mobility control by creating new connections and neuropathways, called maps. I practiced and practiced. I can't say I became ambidextrous but people who received letters and notes from me could read them! My brain successfully created neural connections that enabled motor coordination of my left hand.

There is a lot I wish I had known during the initial stages of recovery, primarily that more support was available following discharge. In addition to the help I needed to relearn words and improve my memory, I was desperately in need of emotional support. I was not aware there were support groups, neuropsychiatrists, and psychotherapists who understand how to treat longer-term TBI recovery. I was not well enough to know who to ask or where to conduct research. Instead, I found myself sinking lower and lower into desperate isolation, loneliness, and even thoughts of suicide.

I wanted and needed to cry but held back the tears daily. When I cried, I would frequently think to myself, "If only I had someone to talk to." As I look back, I realize how hard I worked to not discuss the accident and the feeling of isolation I had as a result. I had walked away from all my friends. Multiple misunderstandings in family communication and behaviors led me to believe I had been abandoned by those I was closest to and needed the most.

Three years into recovery, as part of my self-prescribed recovery plan, I found a neuropsychiatrist and psychotherapist who were both well versed in TBI and co-morbidities with mental health. I was certain I had not reached optimal brain function and decided to prove it, with the support of my neuropsychiatrist and therapist. I had learned by way of my physical improvements that I could beat the time frames presented to me by physicians and other professionals. I did not use the wheelchair, walker, or crutches for nearly as long as had been estimated. I have always been competitive and was delighted to find myself beating every estimated timeline. Though ready to take it on, I was not as hopeful about improving my brain function.

At the time of discharge, I still needed to relearn hundreds of words. There were only a few times it seemed I was learning a word for the first time. In most cases, I realized I had used the words in the past. In addition to missing hundreds of words from my vocabulary, both short-term and long-term memory were significantly impaired. It is common that short-term memory is disabled by TBIs. For me, it was both short-term and long-term. Word retrieval was a maddening challenge, even for words used daily. Brain fatigue set in every day, typically after 1:00 PM, and brain function shutdowns were not uncommon.

On three occasions, a full brain shutdown occurred while I was driving. I suddenly did not know where I was or where I was going. I have no clue how, but I relied on what I now consider an override ability. The words I spoke out loud were, "Don't panic. Do not take your eyes off the road. Find a way to safely stop the car." The first time this happened, I sat in the car for close to an hour in complete disbelief and terror. I was going to contact someone to come get me, or at least contact AAA to tow the car. I did neither, as I realized I was again using my prefrontal cortex (the higher functioning part of our brains). I knew where I was, who I was, and even where I was driving to. Similar incidents occurred two additional times. Panic and terror were significantly reduced at the time of the second and third incidents. As a result of the TBI, my license had been revoked for several months. Documentation indicated the license would not be valid for six months to a year, and only once I passed both driving and written exams. I contacted the Department of Motor Vehicles Medical Advisory Board and begged to have the examinations scheduled prior to six months. My request was granted and I started to drive as soon as I was informed I had passed.

About one and a half years into recovery, I returned to the trail I trained on for the Iron Girl Triathlon. As friends and family learned I was on the trail, I would frequently get comments about how wonderful it was that I was back to jogging. My standard response was to explain that I wouldn't call it a jog; maybe more of a hobble-jog because I continued to have a limp.

At almost the same time, I accepted an invitation to serve as the opening keynote speaker at a conference of 450 people. Public speaking and training had been components of my career for 36 years. I had not worked in about one and a half years and assumed I was ready to get back to public speaking, executive and physician leadership coaching, and workplace mediation. I returned to work far too soon and the evaluations of my performance on that stage were verification. Some of what was written in the comment section created pain greater than broken bones and a cracked skull. I was devastated and proclaimed that I would never again get on a stage and speak publicly.

As I'm sure was part of my prescribed life journey, shortly after making this proclamation, I sat in an audience listening to Brené Brown give the keynote address. It was as if she was looking directly into my eyes as she said something along the lines of, "Yes, you are going to fall down when you are in that arena presenting. You will fall hard, and it will hurt. You will then get yourself up, brush yourself off and get BACK INTO THAT ARENA!"

I was mesmerized. And then of all things, Brené and I rode up the hotel elevator, just the two of us, for 12 floors. I thanked her for her outstanding presentation and told her I knew what I heard was going to change my life going forward. Sometimes I look back and cannot believe I asked her for a hug. She smiled and said, "Absolutely. Get on over here." I can still feel that hug!

Then, one day when I was on a hobble-jog, it hit me that any one of us might at some point in our lives need to hobble-jog. Whether it is physical, emotional, spiritual, relational, or psychological - we might have to hobble-jog. It also hit me that needing to hobble-jog did not preclude me from crossing the finish line. I may not run as fast as I once did, but that does not mean I can't keep moving forward and cross the finish line. I have always been competitive. One of the valuable lessons learned through my continued leg disability is that when I compete with others, there will always be someone better.

I began to see the value of connecting with the power in me to strive to do the best I can, keeping the competition within while getting stronger each day. Courage has been with me always and that's what it took. I drew on my courage to get up and be here, doing the best I can in life.

As I continued to hobble-jog, I repeatedly asked, "Why am I here? Why didn't I complete the dying process? I wouldn't be here if there was not something I am meant to do, but what is it?" I woke up asking myself these questions, and I went to sleep asking them again. I have a friend I used to call my "woo-woo" friend who suggested that I stop making so much noise about it. If I could learn to slow down and reduce the vibrations surrounding my body and spirit, the answer might show up. "Just be quiet Susan, and if there is a message, it will get through!"

As I thought more about the hobble-jog analogy, I decided that I wanted to do something with all the learning that had taken place since my near-death experience. I wanted to encourage and support others who felt as I did when I was in that bed aching from head to toe, not wanting to face the reality of what happened to my body and brain.

Triumph

At six and a half years after the accident, my journey through recovery landed me at a place I considered triumphant. It was at that time my oldest sister said to me, "Susan, if I didn't know, I wouldn't know." When you have someone who knows you say those words, optimism begins to govern how you move forward. At eight years in recovery, my brain may still not function at pre-accident levels, and that's okay. My optimism, courage, and drive will stimulate further advances.

Where it All Began

This book and my chapter are dedicated to my sister Karin who suffered from stage four lung cancer for 10+ years. I was frustrated every day by not being able to "do something" to help Karin. "Doing" has been a main driver in my life. What could I "do' to make a difference? I decided to raise funds for Karin's out-of-pocket medical expenses. I did so by participating in something I had never in my life imagined doing, a triathlon. As part of racing in the 2013 Iron Girl Triathlon in Maryland, I raised funds for Karin. One of my dearest friends trained with me, and never stopped encouraging me. If not for her, I'm not sure completing a triathlon would have happened. I raced with others in the water, on bikes, and by foot. Crossing the finish line gave me a feeling of triumph, for Karin and for me.

On March 28, 2016, from her bed in the hospital, Karin said, "I need to go home now." She closed her eyes, and shortly thereafter, she passed. HobbleJog Foundation was initially named *Racing for Karin*.

Pay It Forward

On July 26, 2016, HobbleJog Foundation was launched and in the first five years presented eight grants that are funding what might be one of the answers to the "Now What?" question. The answer was to pay it forward by presenting grants to post-acute service providers dedicated to helping TBI survivors thrive. Surviving is one thing. Thriving reveals an image of the survivor's heightened determination to remain in forward motion, achieving triumphant outcomes.

My vision is that no one in recovery from a TBI will find themselves unable to continue their recovery following acute treatment. Our 501(c)(3) nonprofit presents grants to fund post-acute resources for TBI survivors.

"Stay bold, brave, and determined.
Don't let anyone or anything
tell you triumph is out of your reach.
Keep moving forward
and never, never, never give up!"

Susan M. Hahn
Maryland

Resources
that helped Susan

<u>My Brain-Strengthening Treatment Plan</u>

Online research lifted my spirits tremendously. There are more programs, games, exercises, and education than I could have imagined. I began using, and continue to access:

Lumosity - Efficacy studies have found significant improvement in cognitive performance for individuals who access Lumosity exercises and education. There is no fee and no end to the number of ways you can work the brain muscle. <u>www.lumosity.com</u>

Wii Brain Games/Nintendo - Wii offers Nintendo brain games to play with others and single-player tests and games. You can track your results and re-take any test as many times as you want. The most beneficial online exercises for me were those focused on pattern recognition. You can choose to start with minimal match requirements and gradually increase the number of matches.

<u>www.play.nintendo.com/activities/memory-match/pikmin-3-deluxe-memory-match-game</u>

Disney Brain Games on TV - Fun to watch brain games and exercises that improve memory through tests. You participate in memory competitions while TV guests do the same. Note: not all episodes offer practical learning. Watching the first three minutes of any episode will reveal whether there will be valuable brain training content. Go to www.disneyplus.com and put "brain games" into the search bar.

Brain Training Website - Exercises can be selected based on several categories, including memory, logic, concentration, speed, and perception. I focused primarily on improving my working memory and mental flexibility, www.braingames.com

Neuropsychiatrist and Neuropsychologist or psychotherapist well versed in TBI and comorbidities with mental health. The therapist I chose is a Psychiatric Nurse and therapy continues. The role of the psychiatrist is to conduct a thorough evaluation and then ongoing medication management, not psychotherapy. Being evaluated and monitored by a psychiatrist and working with a psychotherapist are the two most beneficial post-acute resources I can recommend! I knew they existed but initially had no energy or focus to begin a search. It wasn't until about four years into recovery that my search began. I interviewed several psychiatrists and psychotherapists before finding the right "fits" for me.

About Susan M. Hahn

Since the early 1980s, Susan's work has focused on helping others. Prior to starting her coaching and consulting firm in 2001, she worked for 17 years for a behavioral health system. Over that time, she served as a clinician, manager, director, Vice President and Chief Operating Officer. Her academic degrees and licenses create a bridge between psychology and business management.

Susan continues to provide executive and physician leadership coaching, training, and workplace mediation. Her firm also trains coaches and trainers best practices in use of psychometric profiling instruments, most notably Everything DiSC and the Five Behaviors by Wiley Publishing.

Six weeks after completing her first ever triathlon in 2013, Susan was hit by a speeding car. By far the most difficult injury for Susan to accept and recover from was a traumatic brain injury (TBI). In July 2016 she launched the nonprofit HobbleJog Foundation, dedicated to helping TBI survivors thrive.

Susan's former boss, Steven S. Sharfstein, MD, CEO Emeritus Sheppard Pratt Health System said something to Susan that was both humbling and hopeful, "Susan, you took a major near-death tragedy in your life and turned it into something miraculous for others!"

Chapter 2

Rainbows, Unicorns and Nerdy Resilience

Carrie E. Rickert

I did not see a "white light." Nor did family members, having passed before me, appear to me and tell me it wasn't my time. My life did not flash before my eyes. I didn't experience any of the things that you hear of in "near-death experiences." It isn't that I don't believe that this might happen for some people, but I can say that it did not happen for me. Perhaps, though, that was because it never occurred to me that I was going to die.

I can't say one thing or another was my inspiration to survive. I'm sure my children had a lot to do with it, but mostly, I think it was my mindset. I just didn't think I would die, or that I wouldn't be okay (even if that took a lot of work). So, I sort of willed myself to stay alive, to be okay (or at least to work hard until I was).

What does that say about me? Well, perhaps it says I have unrealistic expectations (rainbows and unicorns anyone?) Or, maybe it says that I am strong-willed and have a stubborn personality - that I am competitive and I really like to win. Possibly it even says that I was heavily clouded by large doses of pain medication, so I really didn't know how bad it was.

But, maybe none of that matters. Perhaps my belief that I would be okay, the medical staff's belief that they could help me, and the goodwill of family and friends was all I needed. What if that is all any of us need?

I don't know why I believed that I would be okay. I just know that it never occurred to me that I wouldn't. And, for the most part, I didn't see doubt on anyone else's face either - not the medical staff, and not the family and friends who visited me. Maybe they bolstered me, or maybe I bolstered them, or maybe it was a combination of both. Who knows?

It's weird to think that almost two full months of my life are a hazy blur, but they are. I am mostly glad that I don't remember, especially the bad stuff. Some of it though, I wish I remembered more.

I remember spending the morning of the accident cleaning up the old entreQuest office, where I worked at the time of the accident. We were throwing stuff away and labeling things for removal or to move it to the new office. I remember talking about who was going to ride with whom to lunch. I remember deciding that Emily was going to ride with me. I remember the conversation that Em and I had in the elevator on the way down to the car.

I **DO NOT** remember anything else from that day. I don't remember walking to the car. I don't remember that it was raining very hard (although I've been told that it was). I don't remember getting in the car, driving, the conversation on the way to lunch, or thankfully, the accident itself.

Most of the first couple of weeks in Shock Trauma were pretty hazy. I know that people came to see me. I know that I had conversations with some of them. I remember snippets here and there. I remember my mom being constant. I remember my brother staying the night and making my mom go home and get some rest. I remember apologizing to Ryan for breaking his wife when he and Emily came to visit. I remember some of the people who came to see me, and some of them I didn't remember until their second or third visit. I remember Tara painting my toes and I remember one of the nurses washing my hair.

Of the staff at Shock Trauma, I don't really remember the doctors or the nurses. I remember their kindness, but I don't really remember names or faces. I remember Clinton. I don't even know exactly what Clinton does at Shock Trauma, but he was in my room every day talking to me and being fun. I think had I truly understood what was going on, he would have made it a lot less scary. He probably did make it a lot less scary, I just didn't know I should be scared.

I don't think I saw myself in a mirror until I was at Sinai. This is probably a good thing since every bone in my face was broken and I didn't see myself until I actually looked like me. I don't remember the pain though. I know I was on some pretty hefty medications, but I don't remember my hand ever hurting, or my head, until I went to Sinai.

I do remember talking to Dr. Jindal before the surgery to repair my aneurysm. I remember him telling me that I might not ever be the same after that surgery, that I would certainly have some kind of stroke. I remember him making sure that I understood the risks going in, but that I also understood that not doing anything about the aneurysm would be worse. I remember asking Dr. Jindal how old he was. At the time, he was 35. It seemed that is old enough to be a brilliant doctor. I don't remember anything of the surgery itself or really anything after the conversation with Dr. Jindal. I just know that it took a lot longer than expected (almost 10 hours) and that everyone was surprised (happily) that I did not have a stroke.

I remember more from Sinai. I remember the therapists, the doctors, the nurses, and everyone who came to see me there. I remember the first time I spent the night by myself (either my mom, dad, or brother stayed with me until then). I remember Emily coming to visit with her mom. I remember thinking how happy I was that neither Em nor her family blamed me for the accident. (Obviously, I know it was an accident and I would never hurt Em on purpose, but still, I remember being glad that they didn't blame me - I blamed myself). I remember the first meal I got to actually eat.

I remember how thrilled the therapists were at my enthusiasm and willingness to try whatever they gave me to try. Evidently, there are many people in a rehab hospital that don't make a lot of effort and become very depressed. That wasn't me. I wanted to work hard. I wanted to go home and be with my children. I wanted my old life back.

As time has gone on, my parents and friends have helped me piece together things I don't remember. It has become somewhat of a blur as to what I remember and what I've been told by others. I doubt it really matters.

I know that I am grateful. I am grateful for everyone who supported me and prayed for me. Mostly though, I am grateful to be alive, that for the most part, I am whole, and that I get to continue to be my kids' mom. I don't focus much on what could have been - I know I am lucky, but beyond that, why dwell on either what happened or what didn't. I'm going to take the good from this experience and move forward.

What Does it Mean to Be Broken?

What does it mean to be broken? Are we talking about body, mind, heart, or spirit? Well, I think that there are different levels of brokenness and even if we are broken, there are ways to compensate.

For example, any adult will tell you they have had their heart broken. And a broken heart can, above many things, teach us how we want to relate to the world... What kind of people we want to be around... And how we want to act towards others. There are some people, though, that do not survive a broken heart. This brings to mind a husband that loses his beloved wife after 50 years together and then dies soon after. Fortunately, most of us can survive a broken heart and it is a rite of passage that children and teens must experience to understand adult relationships.

I was broken in body. Every bone in my face was broken and my hand needed total reconstruction. I will never regain the hearing in my left ear. Most of the things that I normally did on a daily basis I could no longer do. Additionally, I could have and perhaps should have been broken in mind. I had a traumatic brain injury as a result of the accident that should have left me either a total vegetable or at least incredibly decreased in brain function. Fortunately, that did not happen.

I remember, though, my grandmother that had Alzheimer's and the others that were on her ward in the dementia ward. I remember how sad it was. I remember how much I loved who my grandmother used to be and how she was no longer that person. And each day I am thankful that this is not my fate at 37.

So now for the last kind of brokenness: brokenness of spirit. I am of the belief that this is the worst. It is with spirit that one can recover from a broken heart and from a broken body. It is with spirit that I have gone through surgery after surgery, therapy after therapy, and appointment after appointment. While I have truly had the most talented team of doctors, whose skill I will be eternally grateful for, all their skill would mean nothing if I didn't have the spirit to fight brokenness of body and mind. If my spirit had been broken, I would be that vegetable. I would not get to be a parent to my children. I would not get to go back to work. I would not care that people prayed for me and supported me. I would be a shell. For it is spirit that defines a person. Spirit is a feeling of purpose. Spirit is fight and determination. Spirit is enthusiasm for whatever life brings and enthusiasm for making it the best it can be.

While I am incredibly thankful for so many things, it is my spirit that I am most thankful for. It has made all the other stuff possible.

Eight Years and a Pandemic Later

So here I am, eight years later, and I'm sure if you've stuck with me so far, you probably are wondering what now is like. A lot of things have changed and even more have probably remained the same. I am still a single mother to two kids. I started my own consulting business about a year and half after the accident. I started slowly and built it up as I was ready. I have worked primarily from home for the last six and a half years which has allowed me to be flexible for my kids and their needs.

My oldest child left public school after the sixth grade and has been in an online private school since then. He needs a lot of additional educational support so my schedule allows for that. My youngest plays field hockey, both on an outdoor rec team and on a competitive indoor travel team. She keeps me hopping with practice and tournament travel.

I spend the majority of my work time coaching individuals and business owners, and contracting for the Edward Lowe Foundation, working on their Systems for Integrated Growth and other programs as a Team Lead. I absolutely love my job. I get to talk with leaders and companies in all parts of the country and learn about new industries that have the similar challenges that all growing businesses have. This brings me joy on a regular basis.

Things were rolling. I had systems in place to organize and help me. I was operating at the top of my game and I had finally gotten to a point where I didn't think about my accident and the TBI regularly. And then, the pandemic happened. I know the pandemic has been a struggle for most people, and for me it was a truly humbling experience.

I went from the certainty I had created for my days to complete chaos. I went from one child at home, to having to manage two children and their education, as well as keep my clients happy, and not lose my mind, all while being isolated from my support system. My story is not different from a lot of people's pandemic stories. I know we all struggled.

I have had to relearn a lesson from my earlier recovery days. When I do too much at once, have too many things that need to be accomplished, I get brain-tired. Brain-tired is a different kind of exhaustion. It's the level of tired where your body and mind just start shutting down, forcing you to stop. Brain-tired takes days to get through, and lots and lots of rest. I am not particularly good at resting, especially when the world around me is in chaos.

I had to quickly revamp my routine to include downtime. Yes, I scheduled it. Every day I would meditate for at least 15 minutes. And once or twice a week, instead of my typical workouts, I would do restorative yoga and meditate for longer. This would allow my brain the space to regain energy and allow me to do the things that were important. Fortunately, things are now loosening up. My daughter is back in public school five days a week, there are slightly fewer things on my plate, and I am not so isolated. And, I am keeping these practices in place and have added acupuncture. Brain-tiredness is no joke. It stops me from being who I want to be. In order to not get lost in the brain-tired fog, I have to accommodate. I have to build rest into my schedule so that I can work and play as effectively as I want.

"I don't know why I believed that I would be okay. I just know that it never occurred to me that I wouldn't."

Carrie E. Rickert
Maryland

Resources
that helped Carrie

I previously watched a really awesome Ted Talk from Jane McGonigal. She, like me, had a traumatic brain injury. What she did to help herself is quite fascinating.

Without giving too much away (because really, you should watch it), I'll say that her explanations of post-traumatic growth, building resilience, and ways to achieve it made me think of the ways I've helped myself since the accident:

Physical Resilience - For me, this is going to the gym. I went to the gym prior to the accident. In fact, it is one of the things that my doctors believed allowed my body to heal so quickly from such a traumatic injury. And now, it helps my body and my brain continue to heal. Other benefits include being able to handle stress more easily and greater stamina throughout the day. As with everything, I work hard for a reason. All of these benefits are my reasons.

Emotional Resilience - I understand how someone with my kinds of injuries could very easily get mired in feeling sorry for herself. Fortunately, I have been able to get past that. I think this is partially due to my nature - meaning, I'm generally a happy person who looks on the positive side. But, I believe that in this experience I have also chosen to be grateful - for my life, for the people who've made my life possible, for my children, for the little things that I get to experience on a daily basis - actually, for getting to experience anything for that matter. Being grateful may come to me somewhat naturally, but on really hard days, I have to choose it. I know that being bitter and angry about my experiences will do nothing for me moving forward. I know that I cannot have a good life, in whatever way life hands itself to me, if I cannot be happy with what I have, with what I'm given, and for the people who care for me. And if I cannot be happy with those things, I will not ever be able to lead a productive and worthwhile life. That is not acceptable to me. So, I choose to be grateful.

Social Resilience - I have always been a social person. I prefer the company of people over being alone. I like meeting new people. I believe that I can learn something interesting from each new person I meet - and I try to do that. (This pains my introverted friends). I spent a long time in the hospital. The hospital can be a lonely and scary place, even with all the people constantly around. Fortunately, a lot of my family and friends came to visit, sent me messages, or called me. And since I've been home, that hasn't changed. I make time for my family. I make time for my friends. I make time for playing with my children. And they all make time for me. Nothing fills me with greater joy than being around people I love, even if it's only for a couple of minutes.

Mental Resilience - I am a nerd. Once upon a time, I would have denied it - like it's a bad thing. Not anymore. I am a nerd and I love that about me. I like reading and learning new things. I like writing and sharing my thoughts. I have even been playing Ms. McGonigal's game SuperBetter. It's pretty cool. I enjoy using my brain. I am so lucky to have one. I have the benefit of understanding just how lucky I am to have a working brain, so I plan to use it - a lot! I spend a lot of time playing brain games, particularly logic and puzzle games. They help keep my brain nimble and ready to work.

Rest - This one is the hardest for me and the one I have to be completely intentional about. I am a go-go-go kind of person. There is always something that needs to be done. But now, because of my brain injury, I have realized that rest is something to be done, also. I schedule rest. And, I make extra room for it when I'm having difficulty in any area of my life. I have started doing restorative yoga at least once a week, and meditations several times a week. Giving myself intentional time to turn off my brain has allowed it to heal and optimizes it when I turn it back on.

About Carrie E. Rickert

Carrie is a thriving TBI Survivor! Carrie brings more than fifteen years of experience, working with 300+ CEOs and small business owners in deep-dive analysis for understanding their concerns, needs, and areas of improvement, for themselves and for their businesses. Once needs are understood, Carrie works with her clients to design the best path forward, building in accountability along the way. Carrie's passion is helping individuals grow in their careers and personal lives to ultimately achieve fulfillment, peace, and joy in all aspects of their lives.

Carrie's work as a coach, in leadership development, organizational growth strategy, and roundtable facilitation, plus her own experience as a traumatic brain injury survivor and her deep understanding of the individuality that makes up each human being makes her a great coach and partner in aligning purpose to practice.

Carrie has a BS in Clinical Psychology from Towson University and an MFS in Forensic Sciences from George Washington University.

Chapter 3

Love the Life You Live, and Your Life will Love You Right Back!

James B. Durham III

I am a Traumatic Brain Injury survivor, President and Founder of the TBI One Love organization, public-motivational speaker, global talk show host, and a TIRR Memorial Hermann Hospital representative. On September 22, 2011, my life literally ended when I was on the way home from a team dinner that night and I literally died. That's right I died.

On the way home, I was struck by a vehicle going over the overpass being five lights away from my home. Although wearing a helmet, I suffered a critical head injury and was transported via Life Flight to University Hospital in San Antonio. My prognosis was not good. The injuries were critical and the survival rate was very low. The left portion and lobes of my brain were severely damaged. The areas of language - the ability to understand what others are saying and the ability to communicate myself - were things I might never have again. The areas of short- and long-term memory suffered damage, resulting in a prognosis of not knowing my family, my name, or any part of my former life. As I lay in a coma for nearly five weeks, the doctors treated other injuries and crises in that level of trauma, preparations were made for future outcomes, and my family and friends continued to pray and completely rely on God's help and direction.

The neuro-specialist was asked, "What can be done?"

Dr. Parra frankly said, "It's up to God and James, and James cannot do much right now. He is in God's hands. You need to pray." There was no other option. I was left in God's hands and delivered into the hands of gifted physicians and specialists who also believed in God's ability and the power of prayer!

Prior to the accident, my signature was "One Love" representing my beliefs not only in God and faith, but also in us as a unified group of people needing to love each other and the beautiful earth. "One Love" became the signature and symbol of the love and prayer my family felt surrounding me and them. After all, a prayer is just love of one for another. Taking time out to think of and ask God to help another person. That is love. That love, those prayers, God's grace, the faith of my doctors and family were the determining factor in my survival and the ability to make a difference today. "The three abide: Faith, Hope, and the greatest of these is Love." (1 Corinthians 13:13).

I suddenly began to wake up after nearly five weeks of being in a coma. Not only did I begin to open my eyes for brief moments, but my brother was the first to get a clear response from me through nodding, showing I did understand what he said and asked. Soon I began to speak briefly, knew my family - even their birthdays and ages, and before being transported to the next specialized hospital for brain injury, made a reasonable argument with a doctor on being able to eat!

We don't typically think of "normal" life as phases, but it simply is just that. Birth, childhood, adolescence, teen to young adult, college, marriage, career, family, retirement. It is all broken into phases of a beginning, middle, and ending. We all face them and survive them. However, we forget that when suddenly forced into a new "phase" without our choosing or one we did not plan for, it doesn't mean it will never end, lead to other possibilities, or be the expected outcome we fear. We want to hold on to the last phase even when a "new beginning" can unfold if we choose to see it that way. We want the "normal," yet we ARE all unique in ourselves, in our experiences, in our journeys, and in our life phases.

Traumatic brain injury removes "normal" in an instant. The phases of life in TBI are survival, rehabilitation, pain, confusion, uncertainty, and obstacles forevermore, but they are still phases of beginnings, middles, and ends followed by a repeat of another "new beginning." Rehabilitation of traumatic brain injury (TBI) is a very slow process with little or no certainty of the outcome. I now know each TBI is unique and different. They say, "If you met one TBI, you met one TBI." I also now know that being unique and different means being extraordinary, creative, caring, determined, strong, and a leader of YOU.

During recovery from a traumatic or catastrophic event like traumatic brain injury, things happen either very fast and with little control, or they happen very slowly with little control. It can be overwhelming with the changes and so much to do, or it can be frustrating with little momentum and nothing to do but feel helpless. Every step of the way in my recovery, God opened doors that otherwise would not have been available, continued to make everything happen in perfect timing, and placed the perfect people in my journey. Once awake, there was no time or energy for worry. The second door opened just after I awoke from a coma, swiftly transitioning me to the next beginning. My new life and journey would continue in TIRR Memorial Herman Hospital in Houston, Texas, for the next six weeks.

TIRR specializes in brain and spine rehabilitation and is nationally ranked in the top five of its kind. God intended for me to be under the care of my former hospital, and TIRR was yet another "God Wink" in his plan. TIRR is a very positive place with an energy like no other. Again, the change in perspectives can directly impact the outcome. For those like me who are fortunate to come to a place like TIRR after such a terrible tragic event, on the worst of days, there is something positive that you are unable to ignore. It begins with a change in perspective without choice. In the TBI recovery process, the success rate for those who enter these doors is much higher than those of other treatment programs or those with a delay in rehabilitation therapy. It is not only a hospital for physical healing. The approach is combined with an emotional healing through hope and inspiration. Another part of the treatment approach for TIRR is community, helping others, and involving family and love while there. There are NO coincidences, ONLY "God-incidences." In mythology, Prometheus began a period of reign ruled by the power of love, again "One Love."

A miraculous and fast recovery continued as my family and I returned home to Dallas for a new beginning at outpatient rehabilitation at Centre for Neuroskills (CNS). The "God Winks" continued with almost daily undeniable and obvious appearances (too many to share, that will have to be another book). Within five months of daily therapy, I enrolled in a community college nearby, splitting my day with therapy sessions. I was the first patient ever to do this. Within six months, I was driving again, finished a college course with A grades, and was discharged from all rehabilitation for traumatic brain injury! ALL was thought to be lost in the darkest of days for my family had little hope and the most horrible of expectations. Ten months of uncertainty, confusion, changes to everything we all knew before, fears beyond imagination for the future were transformed into bright days, hope in all things possible, gifts beyond any expectations, clarity in what is important, a sense of peace and security in God being in complete control, the most humbling acts of kindness and the greatest amount of love and prayers imaginable - and this is just the beginning! GOD IS GOOD! The gifts continued throughout my journey, ending with a result that was NOT even close to the initial expectations!

Look ahead and know that everything the future holds is possible. You can't prepare, you can't plan, you can't see ahead. You have absolutely no control at times and are in your darkest hours regardless of the situation you face, and that is when you have to change your perspective to survive. When you have no choice, when you find yourself in despair, your ONLY option is to find the gifts in that situation, to find what's positive, to find that hope means seeing possibilities. A change in perspective follows and becomes a habit if you train it. That is where the true gifts and transformation happen. Hope is sparked by and itself sparks positives that light a fire into desire and a will to achieve or see the possibilities. The acceptance of TODAY as just today, not as tomorrow or future tomorrows, is a necessity. Every day accomplished is a day survived (as mine were), or one step closer to your goal. As each day closes, you have a chance to begin a new one tomorrow, make a change, be another day closer to an end, followed by another new beginning. A positive mindset and perspective is within YOUR control, even when control of the situation is not. In all things, a positive mind leads to a positive life! The first step in changing your perspective is faith. In every situation and phase in life, no matter the degree of crisis, your ability to see things differently and create a different outcome is simply trusting and knowing God is with you. It simply starts there. It doesn't mean you sit back and wait, or do nothing. It does mean, even in those times when you can only do nothing, God is leading you to a place unknown to you or your imagination. It is a surrender of worry and anxiety, not a surrender of effort. Faith is an acceptance of, and belief that ALL outcomes have purpose and can be/will be positive or lead in that direction. It is a peace delivered not to protect you from or remove tragic events, but to give you strength to endure them. We cannot know what will come or see what lies ahead. We can only see to the next turn or to the hill in front of us. Faith is believing the other side doesn't have to be horrible. It might just be beautiful.

Hopefully, few will feel the extremes of this type of life event, leaving you with points of reflection and the simple joy of being alive each day. The same keys can be applied to anything you find yourself facing, regardless of the intensity. The gifts, the possibilities, your ability is still there in everything. You just have to see it and do it, and then you will have it and be able to give it to others.

In my life, a change of perspective meant everything! My attitude and that of my family had dramatic effects on my outcome. At the onset of the first medical briefing in the hospital, my family was instructed not to discuss anything about my condition or prognosis within my room even though I was in a coma. "Nothing but positive statements to him or about him" was paramount. Coma patients might be able to hear even though we don't really know. A negative prognosis or even awareness of their present condition can cause the person to give up, to not want to live, or cause pain to their family and loved ones. While in a coma, positive thoughts and perspectives can affect living or dying. If a change in how we see things has that much impact, why can't we realize it in all situations? You can through faith, hope, acceptance, determination, and embracing you and your unique abilities. It's a focus on what you have, not what you don't have. Physical, financial, property, opportunity, life. In all things!

I was blessed with a family of faith and examples of positivity. We strongly believe and were raised to believe, that everything has a purpose and happens for a reason. Every person you meet has an impact on your life and a purpose in crossing your path. I might have started a little ahead in that department. I was blessed with friends who were disabled and with my own learning differences in school. These experiences possibly helped me to accept my now extreme differences with a TBI. I also was thankful to just be alive each morning! Although it might have been a small part within my being from my former life, God allowed it to be so apparent and purposeful for others to understand through my journey. The people that came into my life, my accident, my journey to recovery, and during my life before, all had purpose that now is easily seen by us all. The initial circumstance might not have been part of the plan or purposeful; however, the survival, the prayers, the love, the gifts, all the things that make up the puzzle were and are without doubt or explanation nothing other than a plan greater than any expected or hoped for.

The "normal" life for a person with my injury is years of therapy and rehabilitation, long-term care leaving families in emotional, financial, and physical hardships as well as the person suffering the injury. There is nothing normal about it. It is different in every way and certainly not positive. However, in focusing on the positives, the small goals and accomplishments treated the same as the big ones, taking each day as it comes and being thankful for it, embracing each day as a new beginning and welcoming it, a strong faith in God having a hand in everything regardless of what it is, and focusing on helping others, something so horrible in my life has been changed from "TBI: Traumatic Brain Injury" to "TBI: This Beautiful Injury." Never would I have imagined saying, thinking, writing, or feeling this way about such an event. Who would? Maybe that is the purpose in my miraculous recovery and ability to see it this way and share it.

Against all odds and with many things different for me on all levels, I am blessed. I am now able to share this experience with others. I am now able to make a difference and help others with brain injuries. I am now able to help others change perspectives in all aspects of their lives, and I am now able to appreciate the gifts I have been given. I learned to be positive, determined, led by faith, hope, and love. I strive to find something positive each day, help others always, accept and find new and positive approaches or outlooks, share kindness and gratitude. I appreciate having each day, the people in my life, the many gifts God has delivered, the ability to help others. I enjoy sharing with others in all situations, having an effective voice and positive forum for others affected by brain injury on a global scale, and sharing my testimony for all. I am blessed. I literally had my life end and a totally new life begin. It was not planned. It was not desired. It was not easy. It will forever be different from anything planned or known before. In what "normally" is a lifetime recovery, after ten months I was back in college full time. A year later, I was working at TIRR as an intern. Two years after, I graduated with an AA and was the first student ever to give the graduation commencement speech. After three years, I was attending Florida State University and had started TBI One Love. The patient who would not be able to speak or have language capabilities became a motivational speaker, mentoring youth and those touched by TBI, and soon would graduate with a bachelor's degree in professional communication.

The organization became a leading voice for brain injury survivors, including a podcast show three times a month interviewing leading scientists, therapists, and survivors. The gifts of people and opportunities have been profound and endless. The best is yet to come; and the best so far... meeting my soulmate. In 2017, six years into my recovery, I married my wife Alina. None of this would have been possible or part of my life had this horrible tragic event not happened. God was there and is there, for you as much as for me. If something so dark can become something so bright, it IS possible in every situation. The "normal" thought process is that it cannot be possible. The "different" thought process is all things are possible, if we believe. It takes strength to start. Sometimes you do have the opportunity to make a choice to do something differently for a different outcome. That is up to you!

All things, all goals, all abilities are unique and different, and sometimes being different and unique allows you to do, be, or have something unique, possibly never dreamed of. The obvious: anything is possible. Even "Impossible" can become "I'm possible."

Change begins at the end of your comfort zone, so if you are feeling uncomfortable, know the change taking place is a new beginning to something extraordinary.

Try to remember, no matter what obstacles you face, we are too blessed to be stressed because every day is a gift, which is why it is called the present.

Have a blessed day,

One love

James Durham

TBI One Love

"Love the life you live, and your life will love you back."

James Durham
Texas

About James B. Durham III

On Sept 22, 2011 life as James Durham knew it ended. A motorcycle accident in San Antonio, Texas resulted in life-threatening injuries including a critical severe traumatic brain injury (TBI) and a very poor prognosis with a low survival percentage. Clinging to life in a coma for five weeks, a large portion of his skull removed for swelling and multiple critical issues, James not only survived, he awoke speaking, remembering, and defying everything expected.

The man suffering severe damage to the speech and language areas of the brain, nearly losing his life and the expected loss of all abilities to communicate, not only survived but would soon find success in life by graduating college, reaching thousands as an inspiring speaker, sharing his story, experience, testimony, as an advocate for disability and brain injury, hosting an international radio show, being happily married, and teaching and mentoring others into achieving the same positive success in their lives.

Today, James inspires thousands through his story and example of overcoming great obstacles regarding brain injury and trauma but also in ALL aspects of life. Fulfilling his new purpose helping others, sharing his journey and message of positivity, faith, determination, and traumatic brain injury James continues to impact everyone he encounters. He is an influential advocate for brain injury and hidden disabilities, a successful national and international talk podcast show host, mentor, motivational speaker and trainer, founder of the non-profit organization TBI One Love, and a great support to those touched by brain injury and/or trauma.

Today, James refers to his TBI as This Beautiful Injury and example of the ability to turn horrible circumstances into positive ones. Overcoming monumental obstacles, life-threatening injuries, and a severe traumatic brain injury, James is a living example of survival, determination, faith, positive attitude, prayer, and belief in our God-given abilities.

Founded through his experience, TBI One Love is his passion. Managed by James, the organization is a leading source of inspiration, connection, education, and support for those touched by brain injury. The organization's main website offers a free positive forum for other TBI survivors to connect, inspire others, and gain information by showcasing more than 350 survivor stories from 14 countries, all with individual relationships with James. Additionally, through speaking, social media, training, and mentoring others, James shares his time, himself, his positive approach, experience, and training, creating a more positive life for others.

www.TBIOneLove.org

Chapter 4

A Funeral and a Miracle

Meighan Lovelace

I invite you to the funeral of my former self and an introduction to the miracle of my disability.

It is November 2015. I am the executive director of the nonprofit Mountain Harvest that I started 10 years earlier. I am leading an AmeriCorp NCCC team and overstressing my staff, myself, and my budget.

I built my business from the ground up - creating the groundswell of support, building the infrastructure, raising the money - all with my babies tied to my back. My children grew up on the farm - dirt under their nails and the ability to explain how a plant grows from seed to food before they started school. I was making the impossible possible while working long hours and overextending myself and my family.

I was always going 100 miles an hour 100% of the time. I never gave myself the opportunity to take a step back and enjoy the fruits (and vegetables) of my labor. I would put the kids to bed and then open my computer, staying up late into the night creating programs, boosting fundraising campaigns, and writing report-backs on grant deliverables. I was burned out. My kids needed their mom and I needed to rest. I did not rest. I pushed through all the warning signs of exhaustion so I could continue to build on my accomplishments. I was going to build forever with no exit strategy because that's how you show the world that you are successful - right? Overachieving and overworking had become the standard I held myself to.

But God had other plans for me, I just didn't know it yet.

November 22, 2015. I dropped the kids off with their father and headed out for some "me time" on the ski hill. I was so tired and just wanted to sleep, but the mountain was calling and I thought that some fresh air and exercise would be better than a nap. I should have taken the nap.

Having grown up skiing, it was second nature for me. I grabbed my gear from my truck - looked at my helmet and thought "I don't need that, I am not doing anything too risky" and so off I went without my helmet. If I could go back in time and put that helmet on, I wonder what my life would be like today.

I don't remember the fall, the impact, or even what happened (I was told later it was a hit and run). One minute I was skiing, the next I was gone.

And where I went is the most amazing part of this story. I heard a loud high pitched sound, all I could see was a blinding white light, and then there was the question, "Do you want to stay or go?"

I could not tell where this came from, I just heard it. I was in the most peaceful, calm, blissful state I had ever experienced. There was no worry, no fear, no problems to solve. Somehow in this state of being I understood that all was well - that I could relax and just be. And so I answered the question with, "it doesn't matter, whatever you think."

Without realizing it - I was giving myself over to the will of God. I thought I had died. The peace was just SO PEACEFUL. I saw myself in the hospital bed and thought - why am I seeing this? I was floating over my body.

Then I was back in my body. I did not know how much time had passed or what had happened. I found it so strange that I was back in my body. I could hear people talking so I went to sit up and tell them, "I am fine, everything is fine." But I could not move. I tried to speak but I could not make my lips move. I thought I was dreaming. I would drift away into nothing and then come back for brief moments. I would try to move a finger - telling my finger "move finger" but my finger wouldn't move. I listened to the voices around me talking about rehabilitation, medicine, care for my children. MY CHILDREN????!!!??? I had forgotten most everything about my life. Really - my children? Darn it, I thought, I have to wake up!

Slowly, life came back into my body. I got out of the hospital. I could not talk or walk. I could not read

61

or write - or even pick up a pencil to try. The left side of my body had no feeling. My left eye would not open and the left side of my face drooped down without expression. I was released from the hospital into the care of my ex-husband. Living in a rural community means a lack of competent medical staff and resources, so I was not assigned to a rehabilitation center or given a caregiver. My ex-husband carried me to the bathroom, hand-fed me, and wiped my tears of frustration away. Our children lived with friends until I began to regain my facilities.

I could not ask for what I needed. I could not take care of myself or my family. I could not drive a car to take my kids to school. I could not run my business. My life as I knew it had completely ended and all I could do was surrender. I spent most of the time sleeping. I would drift away back into the nothingness and wonder if I would wake up again. Five minutes of occupational therapy felt like five days. Every effort would zap all of my energy and I would drift away again while tears soaked my pillow. I needed someone to tell me that I didn't have to return to my old self, my old life, my old ideas, beliefs, and expectations. I didn't even understand what those things were anymore. I didn't know what a brain injury was or what it meant to have one. I needed to know it was OK to have a disability. There was no one there to tell me those things.

But there was God and I had faith.

I walked again, it wasn't perfect and I dragged my left side behind me like an unwanted attached twin. My half-smile was both hilarious and scary, but I was smiling. My children cheered for all of my small victories - often saying "I remember when I learned that" and congratulating me with the kind of joy only children have. My speech pathologist would video me and show me my progress while I sobbed in her office - and every week I got better. I started to remember things. I learned to speak again, slow and clumsy, with an impediment I have to this day. But I was getting my voice back. I tried not to try too hard, to give myself grace. To forgive myself and let go of the past. Still, I was angry at myself. How could I have let this happen to me? I was angry at the world. How can everybody else all around me just be going along with their lives when mine seemed to have ended?

But there was God to show me my faith.

The next mountain to climb was reading and writing. My children sat on the edge of my bed after dinner and read to me every night. I would follow along watching my daughter's finger move from word to word. *She* was teaching *me* to read. The full circle was beautiful and filled my heart with gratitude. "You have to find your magic again, Mom, you have to find your owl," my daughter said as she read me the Harry Potter series - warning me before the scary parts - just as I had done with her years before.

One night an owl landed on my balcony. By the end of the series I was reading with the help of a dictionary. Snuggling with my children at bedtime, just being with them without rushing, reminded me of all the precious moments I missed before I hit my head. I was beginning to realize I hadn't knocked myself *out*. I had knocked myself *in*.

God was speaking to me and I was listening.

Just before my accident I was selected as a delegate to attend a National Farmers Union convention and represent Rocky Mountain Farmers Union (RMFU) to advocate for Food and Farm policy. This was a big deal for me as I was a fellow with RMFU at the time and I had worked so hard for the position. I thought I would have to give the position up due to my injury, but when I spoke with the legislative director he said "you committed, it's your job, you earned it, you deserve it, and you will do it," and so I did. I learned how to write again. At first, I just gripped the pen with my fist until I figured out how to use my fingers for writing and taking notes on federal farm policy. With patience and compassion, Bill worked with me on parliamentary procedure, arguing federal policy, and how to sway opinions and votes. Farm policy is how I regained my critical thinking skill sets. What an absurd and interesting way to come back to life. I loved it.

This was a turning point for me in my recovery. I was back in a leadership position but who was I? I didn't LOOK like I had a disability. I quickly realized that all the people around me expected me to perform at the level I had before my accident. I was expected to be who I was before. I didn't know if I should tell them "I have a disability and I need accommodations." What would they think? Would they treat me differently? I had to come to terms with my implicit biases around people with disabilities and my own disability. How did I feel about myself? It was time for me to mourn the loss of me and then let it go. It was time to get excited about all the things that could be - to embrace the next version of myself in all the ways I show up wherever I am.

So I stood at the microphone, with my speech impediment and my funny walk, and spoke to a room with thousands of people from all over the United States, most in opposition to my argument. I held my head high and asked God for the grace I needed to move hearts and minds. And then that peace I felt when I knocked myself *in,* returned. I could feel it flowing through my body. I knew I was filled with the holy spirit so I let God speak through me. *"Page 176, Line 7 please add the text - We oppose the mass deportation of any peoples from the United States, regardless of their documentation status."* And I stood and waited. The room stirred. I listened to the counter-arguments and responded. One by one farmers from across America stood up to support the amendment. They told stories of their laborers, who were like family to them, struggling with the immigration process. After hours of arguing, the amendment passed. This amendment rose to the top to become a key argument in immigration policy - even spurring new legislation for immigrant rights.

God had revealed his plan for me. I knew in that moment that I was connected to God and that the Holy Spirit was working through me.

My business went on without me. My program director took over and my apprentice became the program director. I raised $500,000 just before my accident, so the team had everything they needed. That apprentice is now the Executive Director and has grown the organization in so many incredible ways. I gathered my courage and strength, packed my bags, and took a job in Washington DC with National Farmers Union. I worked on the Farm Bill, networked the beltway, and figured out how to walk in heels again. I asked for accommodations, took breaks when I needed them, and learned to live with those constant headaches so typical of a TBI. I failed and learned. I succeeded and learned. I made the connections I needed, moved back to Colorado, and started my consulting firm. I only take clients whose mission I believe in. I am making positive change in the world and I LOVE being a lobbyist.

I still farm with my family. We raise hemp and make CBD products that help my headaches. We raise veggies in containers when it's too cold outside, ride horses on the weekends, and dream about the future. Not a day goes by that I don't praise God for my second chance at life. I am so very grateful. I call Nov. 22, 2015 my second birthday. We celebrate it every year.

What would I change about my journey? Nothing. Sure, it would have been faster and easier to have rehab services, competent medical staff, and a dedicated caregiver. But the things I learned and how I learned them shaped what became the new me. And I am awesome.

"I was beginning to realize I hadn't knocked myself out. I had knocked myself in."

Meighen Lovelace
Colorado

About Meighan Lovelace

Meighen Lovelace lives and farms with her two daughters on Colorado's Western Slope. She founded the Mountain Harvest Coalition - building a community farm and four-season greenhouse for the Vail Valley Salvation Army and providing year-round fresh produce for the food bank. She has since passed that work along to community leaders to pursue a deep dive into Food, Farm, and Equity Policy.

Meighen serves on the Hunger Free Communities Advisory Committee and the Board for the Alliance to End Hunger in Washington DC, the Policy Committee and the Governing Council for the Colorado Blueprint to End Hunger, and served on the Safety Net Sub Committee of the Colorado Behavioral Health Task Force as appointed by the Governor. She serves as the Board Chair for the Colorado Federation of Families for Children's Mental Health. She is currently leading the living expertise committee for the White House Conference on Hunger and Nutrition and is working with the Colorado Cross-Disability Coalition on state legislation.

Chapter 5

An Unexpected Gift

Kristie K. Warren

Have you ever been so excited to receive a gift, only to open it and discover it is something so unexciting and disappointment sets in? Well, I remember being so excited to open a gift from a loved one, only to open it and it was such a boring gift to receive, but years later I'm still using that gift constantly. It is amazing to look back on that day I received the gift, I was so utterly disappointed and downtrodden, yet now I smile and think of that person every time I use the item! What this memory tells me, besides being grateful for anything you receive, is that sometimes gifts you receive at first seem unwanted and you can be filled with different emotions, but that gift can be something you cherish and use for the rest of your life.

Well, one gift I've received, yet very much never wanted, is my traumatic brain injury. Now, this is not some "feel good" recovery story, trying to spin my injury as this gift from God and others should experience this same thing. Absolutely not. I would not wish the last three-plus years on anyone. The struggles, tears, anguish, grief, frustration, and sadness have been the hardest days of my life, but what I'm trying to build as a result of these struggles, has truly been indeed a gift that I do not intend to take for granted or not cherish and use for the rest of my life, and it all started with a crash!

The day of my accident was a typical workday. I was working in commercial real estate and managed private owner's assets from San Clemente, California to Malibu, California. For those out of state, it's a very large territory. I had 25 retail centers and private real estate projects that I managed for investors and trusts. I was crazy busy. I was constantly working on projects, legal documents, and networking. I easily worked on emails, handled problems, helped my assistant, and reviewed files, all while taking a client's call. Multitasking and Kristie were synonymous. I relished how much I was able to take on. I loved shmoozing with clients, being in charge, and even kicking rude brokers out of my office if they were not acting appropriately! I was a go-getter and the day of my accident I had just polished off my resume to attempt a new chapter in my career. I posted to my social media a happy picture of myself and of my shoes with a caption like, "The best accessories for a woman are a smile and some heels!" Beyond cheesy and completely ridiculous, but I was having a fun day and was always looking for a laugh. Sadly, by the end of this day I would most definitely not be laughing.

I'll never forget the sound of the crash. The feeling of my head whipping back and forth still *stars* in the nightmares I experience. I knew instantly I was truly not ok and my life was forever changed. I sat there stunned. I was just trying to end my day happily and meet a friend for happy hour! This was definitely not a happy hour any longer. I was able to muster up the strength to text my friend I was in an accident as I was exiting the freeway and I have no idea how long it took, but I remember her coming onto the freeway and talking to the man responsible and the policeman. I do not remember anything else. She made sure I got to the hospital.

I shall spare the details of all the hospital ER visits I had to have as a result of my injury, but one thing rings true from all the times I had doctors send me there due to my deteriorating condition during my recovery. Doctors and nurses cannot always give you answers. God love them, but the brain is a very confusing and mysterious thing, and I had more "I'm sorry there's nothing more we can do," talks with them than I ever thought possible. It was defeating.

Sometimes finding the right care can be a challenge, but my faith was strong and I wasn't going to give up. My first neurologist gave me terrible care.

The same friend that came to me on the freeway when I had the crash took me to one of my first appointments. I complained that I wasn't "speaking right" and it seemed to be getting worse. I told him I wasn't ok, things were not right with me, and that I needed help. He offered nothing but a couple more medications, disability forms filled out, and a return appointment! I know so many out there have experienced something similar and I just pray many that are reading this that haven't experienced it will never have that "privilege" because it only made me worse. I was eventually told I would need to see the brain injury specialist in Newport Beach, Dr. Ly.

By the time I went to Dr. Ly, I was at one of my lowest points. I could barely communicate verbally. I wrote him a letter saying, "HELP ME! I just want to fight! I just want to be better, please help!" I could barely get the words out reading it. He took the piece of paper from me and read it. He immediately came up with a plan for me, letting me know this would take a team of specialists and it wouldn't be easy. He is an incredible human and I attribute him with saving my life.

In my mind back then, I just wanted to speak correctly and be back at the office! I just wanted to get back to schmoozing and loving life! I remember asking him if I could return to work. "Maybe two months or so, once I fixed my speech?"

He laughed and said, "Um, that's not how this works!" The one thing he then added was, "Your Type A personality will get in the way, so try to slow down, be kind to yourself, and don't push so hard."

"Don't push so hard? Slow down? What the heck kind of advice is this," I thought to myself. Little did I know that I would continue to hear these words years later in my recovery. I only knew one way through things. I pushed. I pushed hard. I fought. I struggled, but I could do this. And I could do it fast. "I'll be back to the old Kristie in no time," I told myself. How could he say such a thing? We Type As put our minds to something and accomplish it. We get the job done! Heck, I'd just had months of recuperating from kidney stones and a vicious ulcer and only missed one day of work! I have been underestimated my whole life, so I figured he just didn't know who he was dealing with when he told me those things! He's the best TBI guy Hoag Hospital has? "Hmm; we shall show him!" I laughed to myself. Spoiler alert: he knew exactly who and what he was dealing with when he said those things!

My plan was laid out by Dr. Ly and that meant I'd have to work with many other specialists. This would include intensive talk therapy, neuropsych evaluations, physical therapy, and speech therapy. He also recommended I apply for an Acquired Brain Injury Program at Coastline College in Newport Beach to learn coping strategies to navigate my new life with my new weaknesses. I had my discharge paperwork and walked out of his door. To this day, every time I see him, I'm given the same paperwork which has listed at the top, "Reasons for Visit: Traumatic Brain Injury, Problem with Gait." This has just always made me laugh. Yes, laugh. You THINK those are reasons to visit a doctor? You'd think I should have understood at that point, that first day, that I was in for a serious future? Nope! I had no clue that just having survived a bad neurologist would not be the worst of what I was about to go through.

I remember having this list he'd given me and having to navigate finding some of these specialists. My first stop was to Courhy and Beuhler Physical Therapy. This was a PT place I had taken both my children to during some hard times and Dr. David Luckett had taken their cases on with such love and concern that I knew I needed to go there first. At this time I couldn't speak well at all. I walked in and saw the head doctor smile. Now I think he knew immediately there was something very wrong with me. I opened my mouth to speak and his face dropped. As I remember this, I can't help but tear up. Along this journey, I cannot tell you how many people's faces I've seen drop just as I try to speak. It's humiliating, humbling, frustrating, and just created a sense of sadness in me that felt as if it touched my soul. TBIs are invisible and many people look quite typical. Besides my gait having issues and thus being a fall risk for years of my new life, you couldn't see scars and I still smiled, but when I opened my mouth, there was no denying there was something very wrong with me. I started to explain what was going on with me. David soon came over and his face was wide-eyed, mouth open, with a look I'll never forget. The look of pity is not something I think many people can experience over and over and over again. What transpired over the next year or so were some of the most painful parts of the recovery.

I'd lie on the table to do a movement and my entire body would shake like a dying fish on a boat. I had no control over my body. My "push through and fight" attitude was being challenged three times a week! I was in the middle of this huge room with people turning their heads to look at me in shock of what they were hearing and seeing. It became obvious that I would need to be treated in a private room due to the many issues I was experiencing.

After about a year, he knew I needed more intensive and specialized treatment, so I went to see a vestibular specialist. The therapy a vestibular specialist would give me was needed, since I was a fall risk, and couldn't tolerate major head movements, got dizzy just trying to get ice out of the refrigerator looking down, and, in short, my eye-brain connection was in bad shape. As hard as it was to leave him, I knew I needed to get my dizziness and stability improved, so more in-depth therapy was needed.

Coury and Buehler were the last specialists I had previous history with, which also meant any feeling of security and safety was now gone. I had to now find all new doctors with no previous treatment history. It was a scary proposition. I had many fails along the way but finally found Brain Wellness Institute in Newport Beach. My first months with Dr. Jaime Spray, psychotherapist, were filled with some truly horrible memories. I'd see her twice a week to try to get out of my head. There would be so many days I'd physically hit my head trying to get words out. I'd sit there with my eyes closed holding my hands on my head unable to get any words out. Tears would pour out of my eyes at a rate and flow I didn't know I was capable of making. Never in my life did I imagine I'd look at myself and see what I had become. I remember saying in the beginning that I just wanted to be "fixed." The beautiful thing about being broken down is the ability to build yourself back up. As I reflect on how hard this part of my recovery was, I value the struggle, as it now gives me strength as I tackle life's ups and downs with my new abilities.

I just wanted to take a magic pill to "fix me!" Why can't they just find what's wrong inside of my brain and make me, *me,* again? Why can't my body just cooperate and fix itself already? I didn't know then just how comfortable I would have to get with not knowing or not having answers.

The search for the magic pill I was looking for led me to Coastline College's Acquired Brain Injury (ABI) Program. It was a four-day a week, four-hour a day program. When I started there I was already doing two days a week at psychotherapy, three days a week at physical therapy, and three days a week at speech therapy, so adding this new program was a huge task. Just like any other task I'd gotten at work before my accident, I thought, "No Problem! I've got this!" Spoiler Alert #2: I most definitely did not have it!

My first day at the program, which I'd call Brain Camp just to add some flair, was intense. The first hour was computers and I could type and communicate in typing so I thought that it was a waste of time. I felt completely out of place, surrounded by people that were very different from me. The second hour was the psychosocial hour. I walked to that room and was met by a man finishing his private speech therapy, a doctor for 34 years, Dr. Eddie Doidge. He looked at me as I sort of slammed my folder down on the desk. He snapped at me, "What's up with that?" I retorted in my stuttering and broken speech, "I don't belong here. This is nuts." He replied, "Well, not only are you F-ing here, you aren't even in the highest performing group!" He proceeded to laugh hysterically! My mouth was on the floor! Not only did I think we'd become best friends because of his abrasive, yet clearly well-articulated comments back to my attitude walking in, but I wasn't even in the BEST and MOST functional group? Talk about a kick to my gut. Of course, I immediately pulled up a chair next to him where he would become so valuable to me as a support, mentor, and friend.

Once that lovely introduction to Brain Camp finished, our psychosocial counselor would come in. Kim was stern, assertive, and no-nonsense. She laid out the rules of the class and spoke of how we'd be working with her to emotionally navigate our new lives. Of course, I had to equal the assertiveness and tell her, "I will only be here for 8 weeks. I just need to get back to work!" Now, I know what you're thinking. Surely by now, I'd understand what I was dealing with in regards to my recovery. NOPE! I had one goal in mind and it was to get myself back to work. Back to shmoozing with people, partying, and enjoying the fruits of my success. The look Kim gave me was priceless! She just said, "Ok, sure, yeah, let's see how this works out!" As she said this, I turned my head to Eddie who was acting as if I was George Carlin doing standup comedy back in the day! Having been in this program over two years, I'm still in awe of how utterly clueless I was! Kim spoke of Post Traumatic Growth and how we may just be able to come out of this better than before. "OMG, this is ridiculous!" I thought. Little did I know, that would be exactly what would happen!

The next two hours is the cognitive portion of the program. The curriculum is fantastic and it has been vital in the success in starting my new life, but those first few weeks were absolutely devastating to me. Erin Crowley was my cognitive counselor and she was to the point, had no problem telling you what your problems were, and is an angel on earth. She preached AWARENESS constantly. I'm pretty sure she spoke about self-awareness and the need to look at us and how we really are 8,762 times. Within the first ten minutes with her my weaknesses were beyond evident. I couldn't listen to her and take notes. I couldn't remember what she'd said two minutes after she said something. Heck, I couldn't even deal with the lighting in the room and had to wear sunglasses constantly! The amount of self awareness I had for my condition was astoundingly low, but by the end of that day I was met with a mirror that would show me a reality that was absolutely horrific to me.

I went home after that first day and cried more than I had in the couple months prior; in my already stressful recovery. I remember telling my now ex-husband that I could no longer pretend I was ok and I'd have to dive into this new life of reflection, acknowledgment of weaknesses, and work this program, "so that I could get back to normal!" Spoiler Alert #3: There'd be no getting back to anything resembling normalcy.

Over the next few months, it got very scary in my head. I felt desperate for a life that wasn't what I was currently experiencing. I'd grown so tired of "being off," of falling, of speaking terribly and getting the pity looks. I was so tired of having to do exercises just to show me what other problems I had. I was exhausted by life. I've never napped as an adult really but I was taking three to four-hour naps after all my therapies. I was just beyond done. There would be times I'd just want someone to hold me and take away the pain, but no one was there. This was my own fight and I was on my own. There were multiple days I could barely make it out of bed or would catch myself on my bathroom floor just bawling, crying out for help, and I'd end up crawling, yes CRAWLING, to the Bible to see if maybe that would be the answer! I'd open it and read the first thing I'd see. I'd cry out to God to just let me quit, put me out of my misery, and that I just wanted to be me again and if that couldn't happen, then end it now.

God had other plans, though. I remember feeling so weak, defeated, confused, and just so, so terrible that I just wanted to end it all. No one understood me. I'd been told to get a Stephen Hawking box to try and help me communicate. I'd been told my speech didn't match my IQ. I'd been told I come off as drunk or mentally retarded by how I spoke. Those things are horrible to hear from loved ones. Yes, loved ones. I was so done getting looks from people. I was so done not understanding what the heck was happening to me and why I just couldn't be better. The anguish I felt so often in those days were some of the darkest times of my life. And while I was suffering during this time, I'd be told to "Go fix your brain." I don't think there is a sentence that hurt so deeply, yet would become such a motivating chant in my head. I knew God would use all this for good; or, at least, I'd hoped He would!

After about a year in Brain Camp, Erin was retiring from almost 30 years of working with the brain-injured at the college. I was devastated. I also was extremely nervous about who would replace her. Along with the depression I wrote about, the anxiety I have as a result of my TBI is top-notch horrible! I played out so many scenarios as to why any replacement for Erin would not work for me. In walked Michelle Wild, another angel on Earth, who was very calm and even-keeled. Clearly, my assertive and no-nonsense ways were not going to mesh with her style. Spoiler Alert #4: We would "mesh" so incredibly well and she is the reason I'm here thriving instead of just surviving.

During that first month with her, she'd tell me that I wouldn't be moving into the best group and that I really needed to work on some things before that would ever be a consideration. I was shocked and so irritated. I just couldn't catch a break! She continued to give me advice and guidance over the past year and a half and has now become a mentor and guide in my journey that I would never want to lose in my life.

She and Kim, the psychosocial counselor, have given me the greatest gifts I could ever receive. They have both sat with me while I cried and processed what was happening in my life, and shown me I'm worthy of the work I'm putting in. They helped me through the loss of a pet, impromptu sale of my home, unexpected engagement of my daughter and subsequent wedding, my divorce, deciding which car to buy, a place to live, and more. As Michelle would focus on basic cognitive skills and what I needed to DO, Kim focused on how I was feeling and how I can take on decisions or the stress of rebuilding. They both showed me that the old Kristie may be gone but this new Kristie is capable and wonderful as-is. They helped me go through the stages of grief of that old life.

Coming to terms with the fact that I'd never get to a point in my recovery where I'd "return to the old Kristie" took so long and so much work. Once I decided to deal with that obvious fact to everyone else, my life started changing. I moved out on my own and would live alone - no kids in my home for the first time in my life. Everything came down to me and living on my own terms. That is extremely daunting to someone who isn't neurotypical, despite how great the accomplishment is, that I could live on my own.

As I came to terms with grieving my old self, I'd realized something incredibly important. I had never loved myself before my accident. I was constantly living for others, needing their approval, and yearning to be liked by all. I'd realized that I could remake myself into the Kristie I knew I was but was never really understood. I knew it would be so hard, but I realized 43 years of the old Kristie and I didn't want her back. I'd spent so much time wanting a life back that I no longer wanted!

Having the realization that I wanted a new me and no longer needed the old way of doing things meant dealing with some serious issues. I had terrible coping skills, I had a lot of demons to tackle from my past, and had to understand that I couldn't change the past and anything I'd done but I could move forward how I wanted to. I started diving deep into myself. I processed with my team, with my doctors, and with the friends I had made at Brain Camp. I started noticing my smile was less fake. I started noticing I was embracing meditation, alternative healing practices, and a natural self-awareness with a reflection approach to my recovery.

As I worked with my therapist to dive into hard topics and work through the pain of it all that year, I also realized something else. I was growing in so many ways. I became calmer. I became more relaxed to be around, and I became a mentor to others. I started to see how I still had all the good of the Kristie I was before my accident and I had a choice as to what else I wanted in this new Kristie. I started building on that.

At the end of that second year, we had to write a paper about our experience at Brain Camp. I wrote and was asked to speak at our graduation. I was terrified. I just started speaking well again and surely speaking on zoom with hundreds watching could not end well. Well, something beautiful happened. I spoke, and cried, beautifully. I was also spoken about. They chose me as student of the year and Kim gave the speech. I heard such amazing words about how I started with that attitude of "eight weeks and out" and how the vulnerability I've shown has been an inspiration to so many. I still get people discussing my speech and how impactful it was. Such a blessing!

In that moment, I realized something else. I was in a business before the accident that was all about presentation. For any issue I had, all I had to do was talk and present myself and I'd get a win. Now, I was jobless, alone 90% of the time, with speech that was hit or miss depending on how tired my brain was, yet I liked who I was!

How could I like myself so damaged and without a future I could count on? Very easily, it turns out. I'd lived so long living for others and caring what they thought. I lived for the chaos that occurred and the drama that I sometimes added because I thrived in that, or so I thought. I had lived so long, so angry, and with a chip on my shoulder. I was finally getting peace and positivity in my life all on my own! I then became incredibly intentional. I told my team, "I'm putting awesome out to get awesome back!" And that mindset filled everything that I was from that point on. If people don't want to add positivity or peace to my life, they can go! I have very real symptoms I have to avoid and I found avoiding anything that caused high emotions just had to go. I didn't want to deal with the increase of headaches, dizziness, and nausea. I didn't want to have to nap for a couple of hours after an interaction that wasn't positive! I wanted a very different future.

And in building that future, I find myself today in a place where I know who I am. I know what I want from life, and I may not be able to have the capacity of a neurotypical person, but I am still very capable of living an extraordinary life. I told many people early on in my recovery that "These are the cards I've been dealt. I've won with bad cards at the poker table. I'll turn this into a winning hand, too." And here I am. I now volunteer for Michelle Wild's nonprofit, BEST, where we bring technology and training to the brain-injured community. I use my previous talent for training and marketing and help bring that to life, to help others who are like me and need help. I write and mentor others in the program and know that I help others to process through their pain.

These days, I find hope in the beauty of the struggle. I have a sense of self I've never had in my life. I take the beautiful aspects of the "old Kristie" before the accident and have blended it with the aspects of self I now have that I never thought were possible to embody. I have utilized the meditations and holistic approaches and blended them with the medical professionals' guidance to treat my whole self. I see goodness in the problems I now experience and even though I can still throw one heck of a pity party, they last shorter and shorter, focusing on how I want to react to the problems instead of the overwhelming issues of the problem itself.

The most triumphant part of my recovery is that I truly want peace and positivity in my life and I crave it in all I do and say to others struggling. I want to give to others and I want to use my gifts to do that. My weaknesses may still be present, but I do not need to be held down by them. I do think that the answers I was looking for from God all those years ago that I just had to be open. Perhaps the bad things we experience are meant to teach us things instead of bringing us the overwhelming pain we all experience. Perhaps the healing I've found in so many different experiences, since I've opened myself up to them, has been another gift. If we close ourselves off to beauty, we'll never find it. If we open ourselves to positivity, we may just find it in everything.

As I remember laughing about post-traumatic growth in the ABI Program and how I couldn't believe anyone could come out of this experience of TBI recovery better than before, I now reflect and realize it is much more possible than I ever realized. I have been through so many experiences since my accident and I value the growth I've made and look forward to continuing to make. I've had many traumatic experiences in life and growing into a better version of myself has been the greatest gift. As I look back on getting that once disappointing gift in my life that I now use constantly, I can only reflect on the similarities. Sometimes the gifts you're given seem terrible, but they just may end up the most wonderful and impactful in your life.

Post-traumatic growth is actually more common than post-traumatic stress, but many have never even heard the term. The growth I have had as a result of this TBI has been immense. I know I'm not the pinnacle of what I can be, but I'm surely laying a foundation I'm incredibly proud of. The hard work, tears, and sweat I've put in to accomplish this have been immense, but it's been so worth it. I know others can accomplish it as well.

Turning a mirror on yourself to look at the harsh realities can be scary and completely overwhelming. Many will not have their speech taken and life completely uprooted to force such a thing, but it can be done. If I can change things like this, I know it's possible for the multitudes. I had no one to rely on but myself and God. Because of that, I have support and people I trust who are on the same page as I am about how they want to be part of my life. Those that left my life make me feel they have journeys that did not line up with mine, and that is ok.

The journey taken may not be the journey expected. Just as a disappointing gift can turn into something you can use for years, something horrible that happens to you does not have to be the end of anything. It may just end up being a catalyst for the greatest gift you could get: growth.

**"These are the cards I've been dealt.
I've won with bad cards at the poker table.
I'll turn this into a winning hand too."**

Kristie K. Warren
California

Resources
that helped Kristie

Acquired Brain Injury Program - *Now offered virtually for many nationwide.*

Coastline College Special Program
(714) 241-6214
https://www.coastline.edu/academics/specialty-offerings/acquired-brain-injury.php

Neurologist - Dr. Andrew Ly, MD - Newport Neurospecialists through Hoag Hospital
(949) 764-1843

Physical Therapy - Coury & Buehler Physical Therapy (714) 256-5074

Vestibular Therapy - Hoag Outpatient Rehabilitation Services (949) 557-0630

Speech Therapy - Expressions Speech Therapy (714) 901-1518

Neuropsychologist, Psychotherapy, & Psychiatry - Brain Wellness Institute
(949) 743-1457

Reiki Healer - *Located in Canada but offers virtual sessions worldwide.*

Taylor Vanderzwet, taylord2nature@gmail.com
Instagram: @taylord2nature

Cognitive Retraining Courses, Webinars, and Workshops -

BEST (Brain Education Strategies Technology) www.bestconnections.org

Life strategies, goal tracking, memory aids, to-do list, & reminders App -

BEST Suite of Apps

Meditation Apps -
- Breethe
- Insight Timer

Yoga for Brain Injury -

Love Your Brain - videos on YouTube & on Instagram: @loveyourbrain

About Kristie K. Warren

Kristie is a mother of two wonderful adult children and wonderful son-in-law and aunt to two amazing nieces. After suffering a traumatic brain injury, Kristie left the world of commercial real estate and now volunteers when her symptoms allow for BEST, a non-profit that works to provide technology and cognitive training to the brain-injured community.

She speaks and shares her story of post-traumatic growth, strength, and resilience internationally. She is passionate about training and developing others to reach heights in their life that they may not feel possible.

When she is not sharing with others, she is usually found on the sand, near Lifeguard Tower 19 in Newport Beach, California.

Find Kristie at:

Email - OurProjectSperanza@gmail.com

Instagram - @Project.Speranza

Chapter 6

Blasts from the Past: Triumph Over Military-Related TBI and PTSD

Pasha Palanker

All I could see was orange. As I lay there, I couldn't feel anything. I didn't know how far the blast had thrown me. I wondered if this was the end and if I was dead. I waited for my soul to exit my body like in an episode of *The Simpsons*.

As I noticed a burning sensation in the back of my legs, I felt that was a good sign. I was alive! And, my legs didn't get blown off. I checked my toes by pressing them into my combat boots - yep, they were still there. As I surveyed the rest of my body, I still had my hands and happily, my manhood was intact!

The other soldiers rushed over to me and were amazed I was still alive after the IED detonated that I had been standing on. Once on the stretcher, I asked to get off and walk back to the humvee. If I was going home, I wanted to walk out of this God-forsaken country. As I rested my helmeted head on the humvee hood, I knew this deployment was ending.

I have to gratefully acknowledge that I survived a blast from an IED (improvised explosive device) that was built with 100 pounds of explosives and 500 pounds of metal when exploded. It left a crater 15 feet wide by six feet deep. Miraculously, none of the thousands of pieces of shrapnel hit me! I was bleeding from my left ear but otherwise, it was a miracle that I was still alive and my body was intact. This was my second traumatic brain injury.

In total, I've suffered four TBIs and severe PTSD. When the first one happened in 2005, there was no talk about TBIs or PTSD that the military personnel suffered. We simply got back to work and acted as if nothing happened.

When you lock eyes with a suicide bomber and have to exit the protection of your humvee gunnery station to engage him, it messes with your mind and emotions as he explodes 10 feet away from you. The blast was so great that it blew my armor away. Yet, we were expected to get out and survey the blast area with body parts everywhere as with every other major bombing scene. It's so surreal. You're shaking in terror because your body just can't cope.

After returning home, I was evaluated for a concussion but there was no mention of TBI or PTSD. I didn't realize the ensuing anger, irritability, road rage, sensitivity to noise, light, and movement were symptoms of TBI and PTSD. I tried to make light of my experiences and tried to laugh them off just so I could go on with my life.

Being married and with four little boys, I started spiraling down without realizing or understanding what was happening. I didn't connect that the slow degradation was from my TBI and PTSD. My life was slowly falling apart without me realizing it, because of the injuries I had sustained. I was eventually deployed back to Iraq in 2015 for the ISIS crisis.

As soon as I stepped back into Iraq, everything that was stuffed down deep inside just came out; rushing like a flood out of me. It was a rough deployment. And then, almost 10 years to the day, I was on this base in the middle of nowhere when a rocket came in. It was not as close to me as the other explosions; it was about 30 feet away and I sustained another TBI.

Because of my previous injuries, this TBI had a much greater impact on me. But this time, in 2015 there was a drastic difference because I was evaluated and received a diagnosis. Coming home from that deployment, I was completely broken from, yet another, TBI and years of mental health neglect.

What saved me was the fact that I did have a loving wife and kids which gave me a reason to keep going. So many of the wounded soldiers end up alone in hopelessness and resort to suicide. I knew I didn't want my sons to grow up without a father as I did. That's when I sought help and things started to slowly improve. It was a dance of two steps forward and one step back. You feel like a failure when you snap at your family and you don't know why. You feel so guilty and tend to isolate or start self-medicating because of the deep depression.

Then in 2017, I got to go through a very intensive TBI/PTSD treatment small group program that was life-changing for me. I learned and began to understand what was happening to me, why I was doing the things that I was doing, and was introduced to some healthy coping mechanisms to deal with it in a healthy way. They even included my wife in my treatment!

Then 2018 was a rough year for me. One of my close friends died in a parachuting accident. My wife had complications with our fourth son and almost hemorrhaged to death. Thankfully, she recovered. Two friends committed suicide and then COVID happened with the isolation from not being able to attend veteran events that had been helping my recovery. This took a toll on my self-care practices which had been such a life-saver.

I was forced to retire from the Army as a Master Sergeant because of my medical condition. In 2020, I hit rock bottom and had to decide to live or choose suicide. Fortunately, I decided to drive myself to the ER and was admitted to a psychiatric ward. There was no stimulation in the ward so that allowed my TBI some respite.

Still being unable to talk about my experiences, I started working on a puzzle 15 hours a day as I could only sleep about 30 minutes at a time. But being in this place gave me enough breathing room to get back to my self-care routines.

I became more and more proactive about my self-care. Doing things that were good for my mind instead of running away from the pain and irritations that tried to pull me back into that dark place.

Some of my self-care was to protect my sleep and pay attention to what I ate, how I exercised, and most importantly, that I take time for self-reflection. I kept a journal. Some days all I could write was the date, but the more and more I wrote, I could reflect on my triggers and learned to stop them before they took me down.

Running really helped me process things. I was becoming proactive instead of reactive when it came to my mental health. Reading books and going through treatment was so healing for me. Any small thing that felt good to me was a great accomplishment and I could see my progress. I was even able to start making amends when I would give into my anger at home and set my intention to apologize to my kids or wife, instead of isolating myself. This was allowing my family to heal and see that I am in the process of healing my wounds.

I was building momentum as I was moving in the right direction! Little by little, I became more functional at home. I had more hope to be my best self with my family! Fortunately, I became a completely different person from 2020 to 2021.

And, 2022 has had such a positive momentum for me.

The most important thing I've realized is wanting things to be better and not doing too much right away. Just focusing on the low-hanging fruit of what I can do right now. All of these steps and self-care practices help - especially when facing a rough patch - so, you can truly live your life and be happy. Even more than just surviving with your injuries; actually thriving. It takes self-care and self-action because you can't rely on anyone else to fix you. It's deeply personal and you have to start small which turns into bigger things.

I am grateful that I went through everything by having to learn how to live with this as it gave me a superpower! You have to become stronger than you ever would have been by learning to live with these invisible wounds. It's not complicated. It's very simple and we tend to take that for granted. Simplicity can make a huge impact when we just show up taking small steps for ourselves every day.

I wish that it was common knowledge what it feels like to suffer emotionally and mentally from head injuries. It's not like a broken arm that can be seen and fixed. These injuries are invisible and brain injury symptoms can come on so very slowly and steadily that you don't notice. If I had been able to recognize the symptoms, I would have caught myself sooner and would not have had to spiral down so far.

There were some veteran resources, but the best resources that I found were StopSoldierSuicide.org and GetHeadstrong.org. These are national organizations with significant resources behind them and that's how they're able to provide this care free of charge.

Reading has been very impactful on my life. Once I decided that I wanted to make things better and change how I was feeling - outside of going to therapy and taking medication - I started listening to basic self-improvement podcasts. I began hearing about different authors who would come on the shows, and then I would pick up their books on audio because I have to be moving in order to process information.

One author is a bit controversial, but he has had a significant impact on my life. Jordan B. Peterson wrote *12 Rules for Life: An Antidote to Chaos*. He used to be a professor of psychology at the University of Toronto. He does not shy away from conflict and that's what makes him controversial but in his book, there is very simple and practical advice that I have implemented. I would say that book is probably responsible for 80% of my recovery, and my doing well!

I feel that my most triumphant moments are being able to spend time with my kids and deal with their rambunctiousness and really enjoy the simple, crazy, noisy, loving moments with my family! They are why I fought so hard to recover and live in a healthy way. That's been a very rewarding triumph!

Now, I've started sharing with other veterans and people who are suffering from TBI and PTSD. I've been invited to speak to groups of veterans and started sharing on my social media to speak out about the topic. Some of my posts are going viral.

The messages and conversations I've had with others have potentially saved some from plans to commit suicide. I have hope, lived hope, and I'm sharing hope!

My kids have been able to see me helping others who struggle like me. Shedding light on a topic that has been so trying for me has been beautiful. Especially fun was an article in *The Sun* tabloid newspaper of an interview with me telling my story. It was the top story among huge celebrities. That's a testament to where this topic is going. These issues are being recognized and people are willing to listen and have these conversations. I appreciate that news outlets are finally willing to write about TBI and PTSD.

My advice would be to know that recovery is very doable and possible. It's also very simple to learn to live with a TBI in a healthy way. It's simple in that it can be easy if you start very small and be consistent. One little habit at a time will transform your life dramatically in a short period of time. You've got to feel that you are making progress and that you're moving in the right direction instead of a self-destructive direction.

The biggest thing that writing did for me was that accountability increased my self-awareness drastically. And it allowed me to process things to understand and get a better picture of what was going on inside of me. Because you can't fight what you can't see. It allowed me to see my inner struggles illuminated.

"Mental Health Matters!
One simple step at a time. Little things
matter. Make yourself better today than you
were yesterday. Focus on today and do the
most good you can, then tomorrow will take
care of itself. "

Pasha Palanker, US Army MSG (ret)
Maryland

Resources
that helped Pasha

Self-Care was very important for my recovery. Self-care can be very simple but profound as little steps are taken every day. Becoming proactive for my mental health.

- Journal for self-reflection every day.
- Nourishment - being mindful of my eating.
- Exercise - being sure that I got enough exercise. Running helped me process things and I could listen to podcasts or audiobooks.
- Working puzzles between bouts of insomnia helped quiet my mind.
- Doing things that were good for my mind instead of running from pain or irritations that were symptoms of my TBIs and PTSD.

Becoming aware that I wanted things to be better allowed me to follow through with making amends with my family when I reacted poorly. They began to see my progress!

Asking myself frequently: *What small thing can I do right now?* And, then follow through. Simple, small things are best practiced daily to recognize our recovery progress.

Reading was 80% of my recovery.

- *12 Rules for Life: An Antidote to Chaos* by Jordan B. Peterson
- Self-improvement podcasts that highlighted authors promoting books that helped my recovery.

Two national organizations that facilitated much of my recovery (especially when they include the spouse/partner):

1. StopSoldierSuicide.org
2. GetHeadstrong.org

Recognizing my triggers to anger or irritations to stop them quickly:

- Sensitivity to light
- Sound; lots of noise
- Movement
- Irritability
- Reactive responses

Simply be proactive rather than reactive with my mental health. Being aware of my downward spirals and moving in a direction that felt better.

Begin helping others who have experienced TBIs and PTSD. Speaking with others in groups or one-on-one. Boldly talking about the struggles and recovery. And, my family witnessing my progress has been a great triumph!

About Pasha Palanker, US Army MSG (ret)

Pasha Palanker is a US Army Master Sergeant (retired) and mental health advocate. He is a recipient of two Purple Hearts for injuries sustained during combat. Pasha has sustained four traumatic brain injuries (TBI) during his military career during combat deployment. His TBIs and PTSD went undiagnosed for more than 10 years. Once diagnosed, he was able to seek treatment and learned how to manage his severe symptoms.

Now enjoying life with his wife, Olga, and their four sons, they are thriving after many years of slow and steady recovery. Pasha believes that mental health matters and he's on a mission to bring this topic to the forefront of open conversation. Always offering hope with small simple steps, Pasha is available for keynote speaking engagements and as a podcast guest as he talks about TBI and PTSD awareness and recovery.

Pasha is a talented and skilled Personal Growth Coach who knows how to connect and drive action. With a focus on growth through adversity, he will help you see challenges as opportunities to build a stronger sense of IDENTITY. Pasha is a member of Skydiving Performance Team FASTRAX and continues to live a very active, fulfilling life in triumphant recovery.

www.PashaPalanker.com

Instagram: https://instagram.com/pashapalanker

Chapter 7

When a TBI is Compounded by C-PTSD

Dina Potter

I had just accomplished something big, something I wasn't sure was even possible when I first moved to the DC area. I had become a homeowner. I wanted to celebrate this with a housewarming party and I wanted to take advantage of the Black Friday sales to decorate for the holidays. After doing some online research, I decided to head to the mall before the stores closed that day, and check out a couch I had my eye on. As I was making my way down the stairs of my new home, all of a sudden I felt myself falling. As I tried to make the landing, I missed the last three stairs and hit my head on the corner of a wall. Hard. I knocked myself out for what felt like an eternity but was probably more like seconds, or a minute or two.

As I realized what had happened, my first instinct was to worry about my arm (which was throbbing). I had already broken it twice, and all I could feel was the pain. My first thought was that it was probably fractured. So, I clumsily reached for my phone and pulled up directions to the nearest urgent care. I got in my car and drove myself there, but I honestly did not remember getting there. Guess I was on autopilot. When I checked in, the nurse and doctors were not worried about my arm (although they did an X-ray just to be sure). They were more worried about the impact the fall had on my head and strongly advised me to follow concussion protocols. I felt fine though, it was just my arm that hurt. I thought they were being overly cautious.

It wasn't until a couple of days later that I woke up with a black eye, vision problems surfaced, I started experiencing headaches, and I started falling asleep at the drop of a hat. I looked like a victim of domestic violence. Each time I fell asleep, it felt like I was having a total system shutdown/reboot. I went back to the doctor, and they tested me. Not only was I experiencing vision problems, I was also having balance issues, dealing with memory, focus, and concentration problems. They ordered me to follow more strict concussion protocols and told me I shouldn't be working.

Unfortunately, there was no one else I could hand my work off to, so I continued to do the work my clients expected of me. This not only impacted my recovery time, but it also triggered my post-traumatic stress.

If you are like me, and experienced childhood trauma, you may want to look into the CDC's Adverse Childhood Experiences Study (ACES), which uncovered a link between childhood trauma and the chronic diseases we develop as adults. I was diagnosed with Complex PTSD years prior to my TBI. C-PTSD is caused by prolonged or chronic trauma and my ACES score is 7/10, what is yours?[1]

The effects of my TBI felt like a double whammy which played out like a tsunami in my head. I was feeling so emotionally dysregulated, completely exhausted some days and yet having insomnia, and then other days, I could barely wake up to walk my dog and eat, I felt like a zombie.

I could barely drive myself anywhere during the day, and it was difficult to even ride in the car at night. Menial tasks that would normally take me a few minutes were now taking me hours and I had to take constant breaks from the computer, especially if I was working on an excel spreadsheet. It was hard keeping all the numbers straight. I had to double, and triple-check my work, because I couldn't trust myself or what I was seeing.

It was all very frustrating, depressing, and making me super anxious. So, I kept going online to seek answers. After doing some research, I found posts on Twitter that showed the overlap of PTSD and TBI symptoms. I was so relieved to know I wasn't going crazy, and just that awareness brought me some comfort. After talking with a friend, she recommended I check into neurofeedback.

---

[1] https://americanspcc.org/take-the-aces-quiz/

Neurofeedback, also called EEG biofeedback or neurotherapy, is a research-proven way to improve brain function through intensive brain training exercises. Although the technology is quite sophisticated, the process is simple, painless, and non-invasive. So, I figured it was worth a shot.

During my first session, I learned what I was dealing with. I learned that a brain with PTSD will have an overactive limbic system, and an underactive brain will have an underactive cortex, and a brain with PTSD and TBI will have both an overactive limbic system and an underactive cortex. It was, in fact, a double whammy!

My first session, I was hooked up to the EEG which created a brain map showing how my injury and PTSD had negatively affected different areas of my brain. After that, my neurofeedback therapist and I focused on training my brain each session, by targeting the problem areas for change. I would normally be talking to my neurofeedback therapist while hooked up to the EEG, and he encouraged me to journal, draw, or doodle while in session and afterward when I got home. I felt a greater sense of calm after each session, and overall improvements (ability to relax more quickly, stress reduction, less anxiety, enhanced mental clarity, and better focus) after about 10 sessions.

In addition to neurofeedback, I have also started the use of intravenous (IV) nutritional therapy. This allows for the delivery of nutrients directly into my bloodstream, bypassing my stomach and intestines (as I deal with longstanding gastrointestinal issues) for one hundred percent (100%) absorption. Many of these nutrients traverse the blood-brain-barrier going directly into the brain for maximum healing. It has been shown that blood levels of vitamin C are dramatically reduced following a traumatic brain injury, so my IV of choice is a Myers Cocktail, which contains B-Complex vitamins, vitamin B12, calcium, magnesium, and vitamin C.[2] I also add glutathione. Glutathione is one of the best-known agents for helping to reduce free radical build-up in brain cells and has shown great promise in reversing many conditions associated with neurodegeneration and TBIs. I can tell you from personal experience that after each infusion, I just feel better (more energized, focused, and clear-headed).

In my search for non-traditional healing methods, I also investigated the use of hyperbaric oxygen therapy. Over the last few years, many new studies have looked at the benefit of hyperbaric oxygen treatments (HBOT) for those suffering from TBI and/or PTSD. One study conducted by Dr. Paul Harsh[3] and published in Medical Gas Research looked at twenty-nine (29) active-duty or retired military personnel with mild TBIs. All participants suffered from post-concussion syndrome, with some suffering from PTSD. After completing forty (40) HBOT treatments, fifty-two percent (52%) of those diagnosed with PTSD no longer met the diagnostic threshold. This could mean that the increased oxygen delivered through a hyperbaric chamber helps heal damaged brain tissue, improving blood flow, reducing inflammation, and promoting the growth of new tissue and blood vessels.

---

[2] https://www.ahajournals.org/doi/full/10.1161/01.STR.32.4.898
[3] https://www.empr.com/home/news/hbot-linked-to-significant-reduction-in-ptsd-symptoms/

Another promising therapy is the use of ketamine, commonly used as an anesthetic and known as the club drug "Special K," especially for those who have not responded to other treatments. Neurotrauma researchers at the UC Gardner Neuroscience Institute co-authored a study that showed that ketamine halted the damaging electrical activity known as "brain tsunamis" after traumatic brain injury. The drug is known to lower your body temperature and improve cerebral blood flow. A 2017 study in Anesthesia & Analgesia suggests that ketamine, may in fact act as a "neuroprotective" agent that can protect the delicate cells of the brain from injury and premature death due to traumatic injury. And according to Dr. John Krystal, chief psychiatrist at Yale Medicine and a leading ketamine researcher, ketamine may also be able to trigger the cortex to regrow essential connections—such as those lost due to brain trauma.

Neurofeedback and IV Therapy have worked wonders for me, and perhaps one day, I will give the hyperbaric oxygen treatment a try. If all else fails, there's always ketamine and the internet (my research has not failed me yet).

Here's to all of us healing a little more each day!

"Healing is often multi-layered, every person is different, and we have to find what is right for each one of us, in order to go from surviving our trauma, to thriving and living life fully."

Dina Potter
Maryland

About Dina Potter

Prior to starting her consulting business, Dina worked for Fortune 500 organizations like Disney, and ADP, as well as in the nonprofit sector. She was born in Guatemala, Central America, and speaks Spanish fluently. Bringing her bilingual skills and bicultural perspective to her work in training and development as well as human resources consulting, she has been helping minority small business clients across multiple industries grow.

A month after moving into her new home, she fell down a flight of stairs, causing a TBI. During the months that followed, Dina learned that what seemed like a small injury, was more difficult to recover from, due to an existing C-PTSD diagnosis. She hopes her experience, and what she learned in her road to recovery, helps others.

Chapter 8

Where Are My Pants?

Patricia Donini

It was Memorial Day weekend 2018. I was living alone in Fairfax, Virginia, in a townhouse I bought when my son and daughter were still living at home with me. My son was now living and working in Pittsburgh, Pennsylvania, and my daughter in New York City. My daughter was with me for the weekend (thank my guardian angel) because I'd had a surgical procedure on my heart on Friday and she had come to accompany me and care for me over the weekend if needed.

The procedure was the next in a series of attempts aimed at getting my heart to start beating regularly and eliminate my irregular heartbeats. This felt like a more risky procedure than some of the others because an expandable tube was to be inserted into a vein and then through that vein directly into my heart to check for blockages/problems, etc. I was anxious about it and so was she. I had stopped all medication including my blood thinner on Wednesday evening and had resumed them as directed by my doctor on Sunday, May 27.

My daughter and I were making dinner plans for Sunday night because Monday was her birthday and we were planning a night out to celebrate. Alice left to work out at the gym and I was home alone. I remember almost nothing about that weekend - from the end of the procedure on Friday, through Saturday and Sunday. My children tell me I seemed "normal" aka happy, engaged, and talkative. I was apparently paying bills and responding to work emails on a laptop at the dining room table. My son tells me we had a long, upbeat, "normal" telephone conversation on Saturday, of which I have no memory. The only thing I remember (vividly) is suddenly finding myself on the stairs to the next level, my face about an inch from the carpet, my left leg shaking uncontrollably, with no ability to stand or move off the stairs.

I felt weighed down. I couldn't get a grip on anything and felt I was going to fall further down the steps. I started to grasp at the individual threads of carpet and that worked for a little bit until I was sweating so profusely that my hand slipped and I let go. I rolled backward down the remaining steps and into the wall, back of the head first. I have a hazy memory of being on the floor somewhere else (probably by the dining room table) and being unable to rise. I later learned the neurosurgeon believed I'd had two strokes - the first likely in the dining room, the second while trying to walk upstairs to lie down.

My daughter tried to text me from the gym and when she got no response, she came home quickly and found me on the landing at the bottom of the stairs. There was a hole in the wall and blood all over the area - the steps, the wall, and my head. I did not respond to her at all. She was frightened and called her father, brother, and 911. Thank goodness she was there because my brain and head were swelling and I would likely have died or suffered more damage if the increasing compression wasn't alleviated soon.

I was taken by ambulance to the emergency room at Inova Fairfax Hospital in northern Virginia, where a neurosurgeon was called in to assess my condition and operate. He drained excess blood around my brain and performed a craniotomy, removing a large piece of my skull so my brain would have space to expand, swell, and heal. I believe that this surgeon saved my life. Later, in my darkest moments, I wondered whether he should have just let me die, so I wouldn't have had to relearn "living" all over again. I no longer feel that way. I have down moments, but generally am happy to be alive.

I remained at the hospital, mostly in intensive care and largely unconscious, for about a month. A tracheal tube was placed in my throat, I was on a ventilator, and had a feeding tube into my stomach. I developed pneumonia and had an allergic reaction to a medication I was given, which gave me hives all over my legs and arms. During the lengthy hospital stay, I had visitors but was unaware.

Meanwhile, questions were being asked every day by various parties - my employer, the health insurance company, family members, and the medical and nursing teams. Everyone wanted answers, opinions, and decisions. All questions fell to my children. They tell me I am lucky I did not wake up because having the trach tube and being on a ventilator was no fun, especially when they had to clean the tube and remove it to do so. They say I woke up in the hospital after several weeks, but I don't remember waking at all. They say I had to relearn to speak and even to use the right side of my body. My son remembers me relearning how to wiggle my toes on my right foot. I don't remember any of it.

My sisters - from Connecticut, New Hampshire, and Georgia all visited me during this time, but I have no memory of their visits. I have no memory of even being at the hospital. My youngest sister says I told her over and over how beautiful she is. She also told me that I appeared to be conscious and wrote, "Where are my pants?" when I realized I was only in a hospital gown. The theme of missing my pants continued after I was allowed to leave rehab and move in with my son and his family in late November. Each time I had an accident and had to go to the local ER, I always seemed to arrive with only a pull-up and no pants. I know this because emergency rooms are not warm, so nurses would always pile blankets on me, sometimes even warming them first.

After a month of unconscious time in acute care, I lived in three different rehabilitation facilities in succession, for a total of six months of in-patient rehab. Each place moved me further north and west to be closer to my son and daughter-in-law in Pittsburgh. Each place was different, with varying pros and cons and each had a skilled nursing component so my medical needs were always monitored.

The most frightening time was at the second rehab when I was told what had happened and then realized how much I had lost. I couldn't walk and didn't even remember how to do so, I couldn't drive, return to my work or to any job, I couldn't even remember how to use my laptop, iPad, or phone. I couldn't see well enough to read very easily. And I was so confused. I kept losing things. I kept thinking, "Why me? Why did this happen to me?

It felt so unfair because I had worked my whole life and had begun to plan for retirement when I reached 70-72. I never envisioned having to stop work, and planned on volunteering or working part-time, followed by lots of time with family, time at the beach, and traveling through Europe and the world.

Then all the other questions began to hit me. What does this mean? How will I hold my grandson? How do I sit on the floor and practice yoga? How do I travel to my timeshare on the beach in Cabo San Lucas, Mexico, or do anything else that I love? I began having severe panic attacks every single day as I realized my previously very full life was now wide open - no appointments, nowhere to go, and nothing to do. I became very angry and depressed. The future seemed bleak and empty, the present felt empty, and I had lost my purpose.

A glimmer of hope did poke through and told me I had better find a new purpose, a new reason for living, and a way to contribute to the world. This became a motivator for me. I was 65 at the time.

Later, as I slowly recovered and began to accept and adapt to my new circumstances, I thought a great deal about how fickle life is. Bad things should happen to bad people. Good people (like me) should be able to continue with their lives and plans! Soon I realized that bad things happen to good people all the time.

My sister Becky told me about someone who is losing her vision slowly due to a condition that is worsening over time. My uncle learned he had lung cancer (he healed) and my dad developed Alzheimer's (he died in October 2019). Then the pandemic started and people began dying of coronavirus (COVID-19) then Black Lives Matter, police profiling, and generalized systemic racism became a huge movement, followed by a group of Trump supporters storming the United States Capitol. A lot of people certainly had more problems than I did and I resolved to not feel sorry for myself and to use my experiences to assist others who may go through the same or other forms of TBI.

Finally, I concluded, Why *not* me? Perhaps I can handle it and God (or my higher power) knows that I can and will survive, made better for this experience. Perhaps it is just arbitrary, but so what? As people say, you must play the hand you are dealt and I became determined to do so.

There were many keys to healing and continuing to heal. First I started to switch my thinking from "how unfair" to at least one positive thing that I was grateful for) every day. Slowly this worked. I had to accept the "differently-abled" me, not the "disabled" I grieved for the old me, talked with friends and family, and began to recognize and tell them what I needed to get better. (Love, support, activities, mental challenges, space, etc.) Part of my healing was realizing I must find a way to accept this new me and working at this over most of my time in rehab. I was in inpatient rehabilitation from June to November of 2018, followed by one year of in-home therapy and two or three weeklong stays at rehab hospitals when I injured myself or needed care while my son and his family were away.

There were two very significant returns to the ER, followed by additional time in rehab. The first was after I fell face-first onto the floor at my son's family's first house. I had been in the middle of trying to sit on the couch, misjudged, and started to come down on the arm. This pitched me forward onto the floor. I broke my nose and two fingers on my only good hand - the right one - rehab was specifically aimed at replacing the cane with a person and linking arms to avoid putting pressure on the broken fingers. The second was when I awakened with severe spasms in my back and couldn't stand. This rehab was aimed at teaching me about proper alignment while sleeping, sitting, and standing. It turned out I had four fractured vertebrae in my back, probably caused by plopping into chairs, not sitting down in a proper and controlled manner.

The EMTs were called to our house one more time when I started to pass out as I was straining to get up from my wheelchair and into my bed. My son and daughter-in-law called them because I apparently went limp, my eyes rolled back, and I was non-responsive. I guess I sort of swooned in my son's arms! I did not go to the hospital this time and recovered while the EMTs were still there.

There was one more trip to the hospital from the third live-in rehab due to a large DVT (deep vein thrombosis) in my left leg which caused pain and swelling. This time the hospital used heparin and then a blood thinner pill (Coumadin) that I could bring back to rehab and keep taking.

The blood thinner I was taking until a few days before the stroke was a newer one called Xarelto. I loved it because there was no weekly blood check to determine the thinness or thickness of my blood and how quickly it would clot. With Coumadin, there is a weekly reading, but the equipment is much simpler now - a finger stick, the blood sample is read by machine, and the reading is transmitted to the lab and my primary care doctor automatically. This has been a consistent routine that my son does with me every Thursday evening.

I participated in physical, occupational, and speech therapy, and worked with a mental health professional I'd known before my stroke, and I began to put even small items on a calendar both to help focus and to feel that sense of "I have things to do."

I had been in a book club with colleagues from George Mason University and suggested that we meet virtually so that I could participate. COVID was actually my friend in this regard because it was risky and difficult to meet in person anyway. The original founder of our club moved out of state and we thought she could participate virtually if she wished. I started listening to the books on audible until I could actually read them again. Now I'm back to reading, using my iPad for brightness and ease.

Then my son started an MBA program and asked if I'd be interested in reading the articles he had been assigned and discussing them with him as he responded to the professors' assignments. I was thrilled because this fit my intellectually deprived brain. I can hardly find the words to describe how much this meant to me! I was learning, intrigued by the process, and I was helping - each of which had been missing since I had to leave my job and retire.

I put small items on my calendar to remember them, but also to feel busy and purposeful. It worked and I began putting every small task on my calendar - like how many laps I walked around the house, read for half an hour, exercised on the compact elliptical, etc. I slowly began to feel productive and purposeful again and my anger and sadness slipped away naturally over time.

My ex-husband (Steven's and Alice's father) had also moved to Pittsburgh and has his own home ten minutes away. He came to the house to care for our grandson a couple of days each week and started saying things like, "Pat, it doesn't get better than this! His words had a great impact on me, too. The impact his comment made was enormous and caused me to stop, reflect, and realize this was true. Life is so changed and it is better! Now we have lots of time with our grandson, lots of time with our son and his wife, both of us have retired, both are enjoying baseball games and birthdays and holidays together with family, plus biweekly dinners out with this gang.

When I was feeling lonely and panicked at rehab, one of my sisters reached out to a local church to see if anyone would be interested in visiting. As a result, I started having visits (separately) from two women on the Leadership team of the Unity Church of Pittsburgh. One mostly talked and listened and we prayed together; the other was a reiki master who did reiki and aromatherapy sessions with me. Both women reminded me of joy and friendship, and their visits helped me manage my fears and relax. Plus, they gave me something to add to the calendar and look forward to. The impact each made was enormous because I liked each of them and their visits were fun and helped me "lighten."

My daughter visited for Thanksgiving in 2018, 2019, and 2020. In 2021 she switched to visiting for Christmas. She moved to Connecticut in 2020 and visits her grandma (my mom) every other weekend. This means a lot, too, because I can't be there, but I know Alice is.

My sisters and I (there are seven of us) arranged a Zoom meeting every Saturday at 3. We've been meeting over Zoom for more than a year now. My book club is even planning our holiday get-together over Zoom this year. Additionally, I booked weekly sessions of chair yoga with one of my sisters, weekly reiki sessions with another (virtual), and monthly mental health sessions with my therapist.

I received both my flu shot and my COVID vaccine in the car in the parking lot of my doctor's office. I mention this because it is amazing that things have a way of working out. At the same time it became difficult for me to visit the doctor and others in person, it became difficult for the world thanks to COVID. So many opportunities became virtual.

My son tells me he has seen my priorities change from work and career advancement to family - and he likes the change. Whether he likes that I live in his home and that he has to assist with getting me into and out of his car for drives to doctors, dentist, haircuts and manicures, restaurants, and anywhere I go, I'm not so sure. It would be far easier for him to live here with his wife and children, and have me visit, but that is not possible anymore. So I am fortunate that he and my daughter-in-law care so much. They love me and know that I need care; they know I don't want to spend my time and money on a rehab facility until I die, and they make a point of assisting in managing my money, preparing nutritious meals, and making sure I drink fluids, take medications twice a day, have clean bedding to sleep on, and so forth. Last week was Thanksgiving and the house was full of family, food, and football. My granddaughter was born November 19 so she was part of the festivities too and my grandson is transitioning into the role of "big brother."

If I had to do it all over again, I would take most of the same actions, but with two significant changes: 1) Ask a lot more questions up front, focusing on what damage is permanent and what can be improved. 2) I would be more thorough in understanding the conditions I might be facing. I've learned that I suffer from something called left neglect, where the "center" has shifted to the right and my left side is out of alignment - almost out of sight. I constantly forget to look left and have found so many LOST things sitting on the bed right next to me on my left. I have a minimal degree of foot drop and minimal subluxation of the left shoulder socket. It was hard to know who to talk with by the time I regained consciousness. I almost wish the children had recorded all of the various doctor conversations along the way, so I could hear all of what was said.

I would have pushed harder with individual therapists, advocating for what I needed specifically and not accepting some of their feedback that my left arm would not be functional again. I find it frustrating that some do not listen to what the patient wants to learn, while others seem to have a set agenda of exercises and don't necessarily modify it based on their patient. I had a wonderful physical therapist at my last rehab facility who was able to observe my occupational therapy sessions and recommend ways to make them work better for me. Insurance required that I work with PT for my legs and OT for my upper body and functions of daily living. This makes sense on some levels but could be more productive if the patient could partner with the therapist on the most important areas of focus.

I returned to that last rehab facility for respite care each time for a week or two when my son and his family vacationed during 2019. I checked to be sure my PT person and my aide would be around and able to work with me. They were both such a good fit. And really helped me make improvements as a result. On the other hand, I could have and should have listened better to therapists who were suggesting things I didn't want to try because they scared me. Now, three years after leaving my last inpatient rehab and moving in with my son, I am less afraid and want more ability. Therapy is no longer available unless my primary care physician recommends outpatient therapy, insurance covers it, and my son can get me there. The other learning is to practice, practice, practice. I had a therapist who made me walk down and up our sloped driveway over and over. I hated it because it scared me a lot. I still feel some fear, but much, much less, and I am proud I can do it.

I learned so much over time within the rehab programs, then continued to learn even more and differently once I came home to my son, daughter-in-law, and grandson with support from home health for about a year. I am still learning. Currently, I am working on trying to return to a regular walking stride. I am also using a compact elliptical machine to exercise my legs and walk laps around the house daily. My left arm is still frozen in place and I will focus on that next. I tried an over-the-door pulley but overdid it and caused pain in my left shoulder. I may try again and approach this activity differently.

There was a long period after the injury when I wished I had died. I told a therapist that I'd even considered overdosing on my painkillers and ending my life. I was put on suicide watch and I was visited by two people who evaluated whether I presented a threat to myself or others (I did not). My painkillers were removed from my easy reach during this time.

I no longer feel this way. I have a new life and have identified a new purpose. In fact, if this chapter helps at least one person recover triumphantly from a TBI, I will be so grateful. I am close to feeling happy in my new life every day. Some days I overflow with happiness.

Because of my age, I have now retired. I spend a lot of time reading with my three-year-old grandson and talking with him. That young man fills my heart with joy. In fact, I worried at first that he would not connect with me because I am different - I can't sit on the floor and play with his cars, trucks, and trains, and I can't pick him up and walk around with him in my arms. But we have our own connections mainly through books, family movies, and lots and lots of talking! His sister was born a week ago and I am looking forward to how he will introduce me to her and how my granddaughter and I will connect. I am joyfully looking forward to building a relationship with her.

If I hadn't had the stroke(s) and subsequent injuries, I would still be working and living in Virginia, and would only get to see my grandchildren on visits (birthdays, thanksgiving and Christmas). I wouldn't be able to hear, "Grandma, I'm home!" when Kenny returns home from preschool. I wouldn't have been part of my granddaughter's birth - Steve and Stacy left for the hospital around 5 a.m. I was here when Josephine was brought home for the first time, and I was here when my grandson met his sister for the first time. There is no money sufficient to replace these experiences and no way to have the same experiences living more than four hours away or even in a care facility.

I can now go to restaurants with the family. I join them for NFL football every Sunday and college football (a love of mine) most Saturdays, plus every holiday - Stacy and Steve host Easter, Thanksgiving and Christmas here because it is simpler for family to travel to us given my modifications.

When Steve and Stacy bought this house and sold their first home, one of the features was a first-floor bedroom and bathroom with a walk-in shower. When they first viewed this house, they came home excited and said, "This house will be perfect for you!" The home setup allows me to be quite independent, but I do need daily assistance carrying things around as well as help toward the end of each shower.

I've learned to put the AFO (ankle foot orthotic) on myself every morning, so I need no help with that anymore. I'm mobile enough to get to the bathroom throughout the day as needed, I dress myself, brush my teeth, and comb/brush my hair. All of this almost feels miraculous given that I couldn't move or speak at all for a long time. So I'm different, but I'm whole! And I'm contributing to my son's family's life and to others.

The Advice I Would Give

Realize that your abilities have likely changed. Try to consciously think of things you are grateful for every single day. Think of the activities you enjoyed before the TBI and look for virtual or other formats that allow you to continue to participate. If you are reading this book, you have survived your TBI and now need to figure out what you will do with your time. Think about things that you love and make them more intentional and consistent. Allow people to help you find new activities that you might enjoy.

"Think of the activities you enjoyed before the TBI and look for virtual or other formats that will allow you to continue to participate."

Pat Donini
Pennsylvania

Resources
that helped Pat

The following resources supported me best in my post-acute recovery:

Stroke Forward Organization founded by Marcia Moran and her book of the same name. Marcia does a podcast on her organization website which was very helpful

https://www.Strokeforward.com

My Stroke of Insight: *A Brain Scientist's Personal Journey* by Jill Bolte Taylor (2009), Penguin Books.

Guidance for Challenging Time - Peace Oracle Cards by Toni Carmine Salerno & Leela J. Williams.

Chair Yoga & Meditation

Virtual Reiki

The Right Hemisphere Support Group - Melissa Johnson PHD - Nazareth College https://naz.zoom.us//j/9024264779. Meets virtually and in person the third Thursday of each month from 7 to 8:30 p.m.

Essential Oils - Wild orange (uplifting and mood-boosting), eucalyptus (relaxes, reduces anxiety, and encourages deep breathing).

Ayurveda Self Care - Abhyanga massage, self-care, and teas to promote calm.

Self-Care - Rose-infused body wash, almond shampoo and conditioner for balance and soothing.

Mental Health Therapist - I worked with this individual on managing anxieties and fears. I learned some evidence-based techniques for slowing breathing and clearing my head.

About Pat Donini

Pat has more than 25 years of experience in Human Resources management and before her TBI, served as Assistant Vice President, Human Resources and Director, Employee Relations, at George Mason University, headquartered in Fairfax, Virginia. She worked for the University from 2003 until her TBI in 2018. Prior to joining the university, she held Human Resources positions of increasing scope and responsibility in the private sector and worked as Principal and Partner at Donini Associates, a Human Resources consulting firm.

Pat's undergraduate degree is in Psychology from the College of New Rochelle in New York her graduate degree is a Master of Arts in interdisciplinary studies with a concentration in Workplace Conflict Analysis and Resolution. Additionally, she completed 24 credits toward a master's degree in Counseling. Pat was training to be a Retirement Coach at the time of her TBI, but decided to retire instead and focus on enjoying life with her family.

Chapter 9

A Love Letter

Laurie Elinoff

Dear Jesse,

I want to tell you a very personal story about a Miracle in Progress. That Miracle in Progress is me, your mom.

My story has a beginning, a middle, and, instead of an ending, we will call it an ongoing chapter. This is a story of my journey with a traumatic brain injury. And truly, Jesse, this is our story, our journey; you have been with me from the beginning - a loving son, wonderful companion, and staunch advocate.

In the beginning, before my brain injury, I was working for a state agency in Maryland called the Division of Vocational Rehabilitation (DVR). The mission of the agency is to work with people with significant disabilities and help them become employed. I worked as a vocational evaluator. So, for example, if a computer programmer had a brain injury and could no longer do some of the analyses in his work, my job was to help Mr. Programmer figure out what other jobs he could do. We would accomplish this with a combination of paper-and-pencil tests, hands-on work samples, interviews, and exploration materials. Then I would write a report with possible job/training recommendations and send the report to his vocational rehabilitation counselor.

I began my career in 1979. I loved my work. In 1987 I received my master's degree from George Washington University in Transition Special Education; Collaborative Vocational Evaluation.

Brain injury became a focus at work and at school. By day at my job, I worked with individuals who were living with all types of disabilities. And I served on a special task force at work, focusing on brain injury. By night, I attended grad school where I took courses and also did a special project on brain injury.

You, my love, were born in 1990. I was so happy to be able to take off work for your first five months.

Fortunately, Dad had his own business with flexible hours. So even when I returned to my job, we were able to share time taking care of you.

Life was good. Dad and I had spent a lot of time in Jamaica in the 1980s when we were trying to get pregnant. And boy were we happy to take you to Jamaica when you came into our lives. You made your first trip to that beautiful island in February 1992. I will always remember the wonderful reception we got when we arrived with you. Many friends on the island knew we were trying to get pregnant for years so when Jesse Benjamin arrived, a star was born.

In 1995 we had to make some life adjustments when Dad and I separated. Most importantly, we did our best to co-parent. Dad and I had shared custody.

You and I stayed in our home on Helmwood Court. I would have you during the week and every other weekend. So our life was moving along. From school to your baseball games, to school talent shows to trips to Ocean City, and more. We were enjoying watching you grow up.

Let's fast forward to the middle of our story.

The date was July 2001 - just two months before the traumatic terrorist attack we remember as 9-11. You and I experienced our own trauma in July of that same year. This event marked the beginning of my 20-year journey living with a TBI.

Our day in July began like any other day. I was all excited about a long weekend in Virginia. I recall stopping on the way to introduce you to a gentleman I was dating at the time. We were only in his office briefly and when we got back into the car, you said, "Mom, he's really smart."

Given the outcome of our weekend, it was pretty ironic that the man you had just met was a neurologist.

Jesse, you and I, had three days of continuous fun during that mini-vacation. Our only obligation was to spend a couple of hours on our first day listening to a pitch about a timeshare - a piece of cake.

After sitting politely through the timeshare story and visiting one of the floor models, we took a little adventure-strolling around Old Williamsburg. The whole area was beautiful and we concluded our visit with a lovely dinner at a restaurant in one of the historic inns.

The next day we boarded a train to go to Busch Gardens. Our day there was awesome! We loved the amusements, the exhibits, and everything at this spectacular theme park. We had actually come to Busch Gardens with Dad a few years earlier. You were two or three at the time. I'm not sure how much you remember that first trip, but by your second trip to Busch Gardens, you were at the ripe old age of 10 and I know you were having a great time.

We really had a super three-day getaway and we decided to dine at Red Lobster before getting back on the road to Maryland.

Some people say there are no accidents or coincidences in life. In other words, everything happens for a reason.

If that's true, I'm still trying to figure out the reason for what happened on our drive home. It's hard because I truly do not remember any details of our accident. I am sure you remember more than I do. So everything I tell you now are things I have been told. They are not things I remember.

Apparently, we were in a car accident and I was thrown from the car. That's strange, in and of itself, because I faithfully wore my seatbelt. So how did I get thrown from the car? Did I unfasten my seatbelt for some reason? I'll never know the answer to that question. Fortunately, there were no other cars involved in the accident.

I have also been told that a doctor was a witness and she immediately called 911. This call prompted a helicopter to swoop down and take me to Shock Trauma in Fairfax, Virginia. Thank G-d you came out without a scratch. I am also very grateful and proud of you because the medical people asked you different questions about me that you were able to answer. And I believe your answers helped me get the care I needed.

Meanwhile, your Dad and I were going through pre-divorce mediation sessions at the same time as our trip. When you called him and told him the news, he immediately called my parents who were living in Randolph, Massachusetts, a small suburb south of Boston.

Your grandparents, G-Ma and G-Pa, got the news, packed a plastic bag, and drove to Shock Trauma in Fairfax Virginia.

The doctors gave them the diagnosis: I incurred a severe brain injury on the right side of the brain. If I were to awaken from my coma, and if I were able to move, this injury on the right side of my brain would affect dexterity and mobility on the left side of my body, as well as my senses and personality. I had no broken bones.

Current Status: Coma.

Prognosis: Unknown.

Would I wake up?

The doctors couldn't give them much hope because they honestly did not know.

This trauma was the beginning of what has become a 20-year recovery process.

So here I was, a professional who had worked with people with brain injuries, trying to help them find jobs. And now, as a result of my accident, I *was* that person with a traumatic brain injury. Due to the severity of my limitations, I would not be able to return to my former employment. So you might ask, "What would life have in store for me?" One thing for sure - I would get to be a stay-at-home mom with the help of your G-Ma and G-Pa.

My recovery began with a four-month coma which took me from a shock trauma unit in Fairfax, Virginia to Levindale Nursing Home and Deaton and Kernan Hospitals, all in Baltimore, Maryland. I'm sure you remember each place from your visits.

Throughout my four months of being in a coma and stays in various facilities, your grandparents came to stay with me every single day. And it's a good thing they did because they made sure I got the best care.

I was extremely blessed to have the love, support, and advocacy of family, friends, and co-workers. And Jesse, you were my first advocate, speaking on my behalf and telling the EMTs at the accident scene exactly what happened immediately before and after the car crash.

My recovery began with your grandparents staying with me all day in the hospital and watching my monitor.

Your G-Pa decided immediately that what I needed was to listen to a boom box with my favorite music on headphones. Keep in mind, I was in a coma. G-Ma thought he was crazy and she thought the nurses might tell him to stop.

A nurse came in and got all excited, pointing to the movement on the monitor. She said that the movement on the monitor showed that I was enjoying the music and he should keep it up.

Similarly, G-Ma sang to me and we got a great response from the monitor. One Friday night, our Rabbi came by with a cantor and sang some of my favorite Shabbat melodies.

The doctors made it clear that it was possible that I would have personality changes. But the monitor showed for sure that my love of music was still strong.

Once they removed the tracheostomy tube from my windpipe, I was able to breathe on my own. That meant that I could be moved from Shock Trauma to a nursing home.

That's when the serious advocacy began. My rehab co-workers were doing everything they could to get me out of the nursing home and into a rehab hospital. I have only one very fleeting memory of being in the nursing home. Of course, the staff wanted to keep me there because I had great insurance. But my friends and colleagues came to my rescue. They were able to coach G-Ma and G-Pa on the steps of advocacy to get me out of that nursing home.

In order to move to a rehab hospital, I had to demonstrate certain things, and thank G-d I was able to do it. I was still deep enough in the coma that I remember nothing of my time in Levindale.

My next stop was Deaton Hospital where I began to have physical, occupational, and speech therapy. At that time I was lightening from my coma. My most significant memory of Deaton was having a big crush on my speech therapist.

I also had a very protective roommate at Deaton. This woman had been there for years and she did not talk but she communicated by using her voice with different sounds.

Well, we knew she was protective of me because if she thought I was distressed or uncomfortable in any way, she would vocalize in such a way that the staff came running.

My final in-house experience was at Kernan Rehabilitation Hospital. At Kernan, I continued to lighten from my coma.

I remember many things about my routine: therapy, playing cards with G-Ma and G-Pa, meals in the dining room, and extra therapy sessions with G-Pa. With the help of the physical therapists at Kernan, your grandpa developed skills as a PT, and with the help of my friends from vocational rehab, he was posting my daily progress so everyone in my life could keep up with my status. Many friends and family members reached out to us, as well.

I spent about two months at Kernan. One funny memory I have is about recreational therapy. I remember teaching the therapist my favorite card games. Would you believe they tried to charge me for recreational therapy? It was weird. They did not inform me that this service was not covered by insurance. Ultimately, we were not charged. But one moral to this story is always make sure that the services you receive are covered by insurance.

I was scheduled to come home in November. During my last couple of weeks at Kernan, I used a walker once and I took a trip to the mall where I learned how to transfer from a wheelchair to a car. Also, the staff from Kernan visited our home and provided a list of things needed to make the house wheelchair accessible.

I made some big improvements once I got home. First I learned how to use a porta-potty. I quickly graduated to using the bathroom with grab bars and a raised toilet seat. First, I had home therapy and a home health aide who would give me bed baths.

I soon developed the skills to grab railings and walk upstairs to take a shower with assistance from Grandma.

G-Pa had his own ideas about making our home accessible. He converted the living room into a combination bedroom/entertainment area with a big-screen TV. He used some wood and made a ramp so I could get from the family room to the garage and into the car. My sister's friend installed an additional railing so I could get up the stairs.

With the help of your grandparents, I was able to be a parent in all the important ways. They helped with so many physical things which allowed me to have time to love you, advise you and discipline you when necessary. My severe injury kept me from working outside the home but it gave me an opportunity to be the best stay-at-home mom I could be.

You may not know this, but your Dad tried to claim that I was an unfit mother due to my limitations. So we had a drama-filled sit-down session with our divorce attorneys. Thank G-d I was able to let them know that my parents were providing the assistance and reasonable accommodations I needed to be a good parent. Bottom line - we continued our shared custody.

I continued with therapy. I graduated from in-home therapy to outpatient therapy. During my therapy at Kessler I received a Triumph of the Human Spirit Award at a big ceremony in New Jersey.

I continued with outpatient therapy for a couple of more years and was using my walker much more than my wheelchair. Your grandpa drove me to every single therapy session. He did that along with golfing three times a week and going dancing with G-Ma every Saturday night.

Your G-Pa and G-Ma loved to dance and I was just like them. If anyone ever asked me what my goals were post-brain-injury, I told them my goal was to dance again.

You know I love to dance and my brain injury did not change that. I've always been a dancing fool - better than being just a fool! Once I was home, I would put on the boombox and dance and exercise. Then on Saturday nights G-Ma and G-Pa would take me dancing at Caesar's, a local nightclub. First I was clearing the path to the dancefloor with my wheelchair and then with my walker. I was back in business. Mind you, I could not dance like I used to but I managed to shake my booty both in and out of my wheelchair.

I have very special memories of chaperoning at your Friday night dances at the Elks Hall and your big middle school dance. The most special part of that memory is that you told me you really wanted me to chaperone. Quite a thrill for your Mom.

Some kids might be embarrassed that their mom used a wheelchair but not my Jesse. You wanted me around, wheelchair and all.

My limitations with concentration, dexterity, mobility, hearing, vision, and speech precluded me from returning to my work as a vocational evaluator. These limitations also precluded me from doing housework like cooking, cleaning, and laundry. Fortunately, I was able to pursue some passions; both old and new.

I continued my passion for reading by participating in two book clubs; one at Temple and another book group that I have been reading with for over 30 years. These dear friends provided food, love, and support to our family when I was in a coma.

I continued involvement in several areas including my Temple Sisterhood, staying involved with your school activities, going out dancing weekly, playing cards with your Grandpa, and going to movies.

I also had a few positive health changes. As miracles would have it, after my accident I no longer needed glasses for reading. On one hand, my eye doctor promised she would never 'ok' me to drive due to my limited field vision. But on the other hand, I can still read and I do not need bifocals.

Another great thing is that before my accident I would get debilitating headaches regularly. After the accident, I had no more headaches. Pre-accident, I was very allergic to ragweed. After the accident, I had no more ragweed allergies!

I developed some new skills and hobbies. I learned how to play mahjong which I am enjoying to this day both online and in person. I also learned how to use a computer. I must confess that before my accident these fingers never touched a computer keyboard. After my accident, I learned some computer basics which have served me well. These skills help me socially when I use search engines to research entertainment options. (I used to be the 'Dial 411 kid' before they started charging.) Now I just google a business and I get their phone number.

I successfully used Google and found the apartment that G-Ma and I would eventually move to after I sold our home on Helmwood Court.

My keyboarding skills help me in my volunteer work. I serve on a number of Governor-appointed councils related to people with disabilities and I also serve on the conference planning committee for the Brain Injury Association of Maryland. I am proud to say that through my work with these organizations, I have had the opportunity to testify before legislators in our state capital of Annapolis.

I have made strides in my ability to use public transportation such as MTA Mobility and Metro Access. I made sure that our apartment was on the Mobility route. Mobility is a service that operates 24/7-365 days a year. It cost $2.10 per ride and it travels to every address in Baltimore City and all my favorite places in Anne Arundel and Baltimore

Counties. Mobility picks me up at my door because my apartment is located within three-quarters of a mile from the local MTA bus route.

I am also blessed to be able to maintain my own apartment with a little assistance. As you know, G-Ma passed over three-and-a-half years ago. I wondered whether I would be able to physically manage but I have been very successful.

I'm so happy that you love my apartment. And no matter if you're living in California or London, you enjoy coming home and having fun with me.

We have had great adventures in D.C. and Baltimore - traveling with Metro Access and MTA Mobility. I wanted you to ride with me as my PCA (Personal Care Attendant) so that you could see how I 'roll.'

Your mom is doing important work for people living with brain injuries through my work with different entities.

I am a member of the Brain Injury Association conference planning committee. Through my work with the Brain Injury Association of Maryland, our family has received several Partnership for Independence and other Awards; Grandma and Grandpa received the Caregiver Award. I received the Advocacy Award and the Frances B. Dexter Award, a great honor and service award.

I am a member of the Governor-appointed Traumatic Brain Injury Advisory Board. On that board, I sit on the S.A.F.E. Committee. SAFE stands for Survivor and Family members Empowered. Our S.A.F.E. Committee worked on and testified on legislation that would help Marylanders with brain injuries.

I have served on the Governor-appointed State Rehabilitation Council. This Council works closely with my work family at the Division of Rehabilitation Services. I loved serving on that Council because I felt like I was back home.

I am an active member of the Independent Living Movement; a movement with a focus on empowering people with disabilities to have control and choice in their lives.

I have served on the Governor-appointed Statewide Independent Living Council and I am a consumer of independent living services at my center for independent living - Accessible Resources for Independence (ARI).

In my life, I have been blessed with good coping skills, a positive attitude, and a sense of humor. These things gave me the ability to cope, find the strength to keep moving, the ability to find the humor and the know-how to face a traumatic and devastating situation, and discover many positive outcomes.

True, I can no longer drive a car.

But, yes, I can still go to all my favorite places and also venture to places I would not drive to on my own with a door-to-door limousine service called Mobility.

True, I could not return to my work as a vocational evaluator.

But, yes, I can continue to serve Marylanders with disabilities through my advocacy and work on various councils and committees.

And I am doing that with some new skills, namely using a computer and giving testimony in Annapolis for important legislation that impacts my people, people with brain injuries.

Twenty years ago I could not make your meals or do your laundry.

But, yes, your grandparents and you made it possible for me to be a parent in every way I could.

I could and did monitor your schoolwork, lay down the law when necessary, be a cheerleader at your baseball games, plan your Bar-Mitzvah, chaperone your dances, go to your high school graduation and college graduation, and follow you while you successfully completed a marathon in Spain. And I could wish you well when your work took you to Los Angeles and now London. I love you and I'm so proud of you.

You, Jesse Fayne, were there with me 20 years ago on the night of our accident. We have been through a lot together and you have been one of my greatest champions. In April you are flying me to London and I am so excited to sit down and have a 'cuppa' as we continue our journey.

Yes, I am living with the results of a traumatic brain injury. But I am so much more than my injury. And you always show me that through your love. Can't wait to see you.

Love and Hugs

OOOOOOOOOO

Mommy

"I want to tell you a very personal story about a Miracle in Progress. That Miracle in Progress is me."

Laurie Elinoff
Maryland

Resources
that helped Laurie

The following list of resources have helped me make choices, take charge and live independently:

Partners in Care - Phone: 410-544-4800

8151 c Ritchie Highway

Partners in Care is a non-profit organization, serving seniors and people with disabilities in Anne Arundel County, Maryland. Members are seniors and people with disabilities.

I called and joined Partners in Care. All the members contribute. My contribution is baking for their events. I bake something and bring it to their office or someone will come and pick it up. Many of the members are also volunteers for the organization. This organization helps people in many ways.

When I was living in my home in Millersville, I lived too far away from the bus stop to easily access public transportation. So I was able to use the ride service offered by Partners in Care.

This program is called Ride Partners. If they can find a volunteer to drive, members are able to request one ride per week. Members must call seven business days in advance to request a ride. I used the ride service frequently a few years ago. This is a free service.

Ride Partners also has a fee-for-service program; using a vehicle with a wheelchair lift.

I also used Partners to fix/adjust and reinstall the railing of my front steps. This program is called Repairs With Care. I really enjoy working with Partners in Care.

Accessible Resources for Independence (A.R.I.) - 1406 Crain Highway,#206, Glen Burnie, Maryland. Director-Katie Collins-Ihrke

Phone: 410-636-2274

kihrke@arinow.org

ARI is a nonprofit cross-disability organization run by and for persons with disabilities. ARI serves consumers in Anne Arundel and Howard Counties.

ARI is one of seven Centers for Independent Living (CIL) in Maryland.

ARI offers five core services and assistive technology:

1. Information and Referral - A consumer may call for information about a service. I learned about accessible transportation (MTA Mobility) and how to search for apartments.
2. Independent Living (IL) Skills Training - For example, if I wanted to learn how to board a train, staff at the CIL would train me.
3. Peer Support - Since the CIL is run by persons with disabilities (PWD), staff can give you support for any situation.
4. Self Advocacy - If I wanted to advocate for my apartment to install an automatic front door opener, the staff at the CIL would guide me in the steps for advocating to my apartment management staff. CIL directors and staff affect systems change and march the halls of Annapolis in an effort to support and create legislation that will break down barriers and open doors for Marylanders with disabilities.
5. Transition - Transition services work in two ways. First, students with disabilities who are making the transition from public school to additional training/ education or employment. Second, individuals who want to make a transition from a nursing

home or institution to their home. CIL staff guide these individuals through the steps of transition.

CILs also provide assistive technology. Consumers can explore different types of technology at their CIL. For example, right now I need an accessible electric can opener. So I will go to my center and check out the technology. Consumers complete financial applications and the cost of their technology is determined based on the info on their application. Both my sister and I have used this service. My sister needed reverse hand controls on her car due to limitations from her stroke. I needed hearing aids and a special phone for those with hearing impairments. We were very fortunate to be able to get the technology we needed from our center for independent living. Timing is important because the money for the Assistive Technology grant does run out. So it is best to call the CIL ASAP so you'll know if your request is feasible at that time. I think A.R.I. is the best-kept secret in the county.

M.T.A. Mobility - Phone: 410-764-8181

One must apply for Mobility services.

To be eligible a person's disability must preclude them from using the standard MTA bus.

Very important - If you become a Mobility customer, they will pick you up at your front door if you live within three-quarters of a mile from the closest bus route. Otherwise, you must get a ride or walk to a location that is near the bus route for a pick-up.

To apply: Print out and complete the Mobility application. The application requires a medical professional, rehab professional, or therapist to complete part of the application to confirm your limitations. This person can also help you complete your portion of the application. You mail in your application.

Mobility will contact you to make an appointment to come into the office in Baltimore for an interview. Mobility will give you transportation to and from the interview if you live within three-quarters of a mile of the closest bus route.

Once you have your interview, you wait to receive your official identification card in the mail. At the interview and on the application state that you want the option of having a personal care assistant (PCA) ride with you on any Mobility rides you might take. This individual will be able to ride free of charge.

Mobility operates 24/7 for 365 days per year. Mobility will take you anywhere the MTA goes. In this case, it goes to any address in Baltimore City. Mobility also goes to places in Anne Arundel and Baltimore Counties where the address is within three-quarters of a mile of the bus route.

Once you become a Mobility customer, you can also apply for visitor status to use similar transportation systems:

1) Metro Access - Phone 301-562-5360 This serves D.C. and Montgomery and P. G. Counties. The cost of each ride varies, based on the distance you are riding. For example, the majority of my rides were approximately $7.00 each way.

2) Regional Transportation Agency - Serves Howard County: Phone: 800-270-9553. Seniors and people with disabilities ride free of charge. Call R.T.A. to apply.

3) Senior Bus - You can ride this County Bus whether or not you ride with Mobility. Phone: 410-222-0022. The senior bus drives seniors and people with disabilities to medically related appointments in

Anne Arundel County and the Major Hospitals in Baltimore. The bus will also drive you to and from the closest senior center. This is a free service and you can also be accompanied by a personal care attendant free of charge. You may reserve one ride per day, back and forth. You must call to reserve your ride at least one week in advance. Also, you must be ready for a return ride by 2 pm, so it's best to make appointments in the morning.

4) **Taxi Access** - Mobility customers can use Taxi Access. Participating cab companies will give you rides to places along the Mobility route. You can call for this service when you want the ride. The cost is $3.00 for the first $40.00 of the fair and after that you pay the standard fair. You may use this service for up to 62 rides per month.

For more information, call Mobility-Customer Care. 410-764-8181 extension 8.

Senior Centers - Centers are located all over the state. They offer college-level courses, all types of exercise classes, great trips, games, resource sharing, and more. Once you join one center, you are automatically a member at every senior center in your county. There is a county bus that will provide you transportation to and from the closest senior center to your home.

The Brain Injury Association of Maryland (BIAMD) Phone: 410-448-2924

BIAMD is a one-stop-shop for all things brain injury. If they do not know the answer, they can tell you who to call. They hold an annual educational conference which is a great opportunity to gather together with the brain injury community of Maryland. We have representation from survivors, family members, caregivers, therapists, doctors, lawyers, service providers, and more. BIAMD holds a check-in chat every Friday from 12-2 pm. This is another great way to meet and talk with other survivors.

Brain Injury Support Groups - You can call BIAMD at 410-448-2924. They can tell you which support group is in your area.

D.O.R.S.-Division of Rehabilitation Services Phone: 410-554-9100 - My DORS work family was incredible throughout my journey. Individuals generously donated their leave time to me. They advocated to have me moved from a nursing home to rehab hospital. They worked with my Dad to post my status using different forms of social media. They instructed my parents on how to apply for

SSDI on my behalf. They helped me stay involved with my advocacy by recommending me to serve on Governor Appointed Councils that serve Marylanders with disabilities. They celebrated my retirement, honoring me at the social event of our annual conference, presenting me with an award in the form of a plaque for my years of service, and being the Honorary Chairperson of the MRA/DORS Social Committee. This was a special honor as I chaired and worked on the social committee for several conferences. The mission of D.O.R.S. involves empowering people with significant disabilities to obtain and maintain employment. This spectacular agency is another best-kept secret in our state.

About Laurie Elinoff

From speech and language therapist to vocational evaluator, Laurie's careers involved working with people to enhance their lives. Laurie has continued this work in her role as advocate and in her position as the 'Governor-Appointed Council Kid.' Laurie has also been very fulfilled through her work on the conference planning committee of the Maryland Brain Injury Association.

In her free time, Laurie can be found playing cards and mahjong, participating in her Temple, book clubs, enjoying family and friends, and always exploring opportunities for live music and dancing.

Chapter 10

Cycling From Tragedy to Triumph

David A. Grant

That split second changed my life forever. The moment I felt the impact of the vehicle as I crossed the road on my bicycle and landed about 50 feet from where I had been riding, I questioned the viability of my life. I didn't want to die!

I had renewed my love of cycling because my health was deteriorating and my doctor instructed me to find a way to lose weight. I had dropped about 100 pounds and was feeling really good. Every day I would cycle about 25-30 miles in my New Hampshire town and countryside.

That day, as with all days, I stopped and looked before crossing any intersections. Every direction appeared to be clear and I moved into the intersection only to be struck by a young driver who had just gotten their license. Before the impact threw me, my helmeted head crushed in the passenger side of the windshield. I remember the sound of my helmet hitting the glass.

When I regained consciousness, I looked up into the faces of passersby who were comforting me and trying to keep me still and calm. I kept repeating to call my wife. A gentleman in the crowd called her with the news and where to find me. As the ambulance came and whisked me away to the trauma hospital, my wife's car fell in line behind us. When we arrived at the hospital and I saw my wife for the first time, the sight of me must have horrified her. But, to me, she had the face of an angel - my angel!

Being the stubborn man that I am, after some tests, I insisted on going home. That day in November 2010, I was determined that this was not going to get the best of me! Even with a broken arm and some lacerations, I was going home. Having only been married for about a year, my wife and I got to work on my recovery. We had no idea what lay ahead for us and how long and difficult this journey would be.

There was limited understanding of TBI or PTSD back in 2010. Sure, they talked about my concussion in later appointments but not as a sustained brain injury that would change my life forever. And, there was little acute care during my initial recovery, so my wife and I felt like we were on our own.

My wife and I laugh at things that might horrify others. Dark humor reigned supreme in the Grant household. But humor is healing. Our humor was healing for me and the grieving process my wife was experiencing for the person I used to be.

I was quite rattled when I got home and knew there was something not right. I had no understanding of how my injuries were adversely affecting me. A couple of months into my recovery, I wanted to bake some brownies for a group gathering and as I reached for the box to read the instructions, I found that I couldn't read! I knew those marks on the box were letters but I couldn't make sense of them.

The neurologist said it was an effect of my concussion and that it may take about six to nine months to get back to normal. So, I hunkered down to get better.

About four months after my accident, I wanted to return to bicycling. As I headed out to ride, I was smothered in overwhelming PTSD. The sheer panic that I felt when I got to any busy intersection almost deterred me from riding. I had to push myself to ride a little further each day. Today, I still live with post-concussion syndrome and PTSD.

The PTSD nightmares were almost nightly. Waking in utter fear and terror in full-body sweats - classic textbook PTSD. Life sucked. Even after my diagnosis of PTSD about four months into recovery, my behavior was different, my actions were different, and I was prone to profanity, outbursts, and saying inappropriate things. I developed a stammer and lost the ability to form complete sentences. I had lost my speech and had to relearn how to speak during that first year.

By this time the doctors pushed out my recovery to five years. I was still happy to know there was an end in sight. I wanted a date to circle on the calendar to return to normalcy. Little did I know, there is never an "end" to healing from a TBI and returning to 100% normal.

That first year of recovery felt like we were flying blind because we were truly on our own. There was no medical professional that was able to help in our area. My wife said it was like living with a newborn in the house with sleep deprivation and dealing with my altered personality and nightmares.

Yet, my wife was my rock through my recovery with a kick in the pants when I needed it and a loving hug when that was needed! Many friends and even our family began pulling away from associating with us because they couldn't deal with the extreme change in who I was. Rumors spread that I was just acting this way for attention because I looked normal on the outside. What is amazing is that even some family members believed these lies.

Linear time has been a difficult concept. I think I'm returning a call from yesterday only to find that the initial call was made three or four months ago. That affected friendships. They thought I had simply given up on our friendship but I didn't know how much time had passed since their call. This can be very frustrating for the injured and their friends or family members.

I reached out to the Brain Injury Association of New Hampshire (BIANH) but they didn't have a local meeting. Until one day, by the hand of God, the BIA began a meeting within walking distance from my home. The first year with that group was pivotal in our healing and we kept tissue companies in business! As we went through the healing process, the tears shed became less over the grief of the lives we had lost.

The days we met were the highlight of our month but we were on our own for the other 29 days. We had become fateful friends - fate brought us together to become friends. We needed a way to connect throughout the month, so I had a lightbulb moment from God in 2013. I started an online group on Facebook, the Brain Injury Hope Network. I began to regularly post resources and information that resonated with me as a brain injury survivor.

As someone who had zero acute care, I saw the great need for long-term post-acute care through peer support. I envisioned this group to be about 100 members but today, nine years later, our community has almost 40,000 members and growing! We don't only support *traumatic* brain injury survivors, we welcome *acquired* brain injury survivors (stroke, drowning, abuse, etc). We want to include as many brain injury survivors as possible in our community.

Always looking to support more TBI/PTSD survivors, my wife and I began our digital *Brain Injury HOPE Magazine* in 2015. Now, this magazine is available in print and in a digital format providing peer-based support and resources.

Wanting to expand sharing my story, I reached out to Brainline.org and wrote an article for them. Now that I've written my 100th article for them, I know my survivor advocacy is reaching a wider audience by expressing how miracles can happen, especially since receiving invitations for keynote speaking engagements at neuro conferences.

One of the biggest challenges for me has been my memory difficulties. I definitely rely on my Google calendar and phone alerts to remind me of what I need to do throughout my day. I find that the greatest help for me is to be around other survivors because it lets me know that others have similar experiences. That connection is cathartic for me.

It took me three years to relearn how to read. It took seven years before I could return to working full-time. I'm still seeing gains in my recovery. So, brain injury survivors must understand that it continues to be a life-long journey.

Today, life is immensely rewarding and mostly comfortable. I've learned to co-exist with the challenges that I continue to face. My definition of recovery has shifted from "when will this be over" to "how can I best live with the subset of challenges that may define me for the rest of my life?"

The best resource I found about six months after my injury was TBIGuide.com from Dr. Glen Johnson, a neurologist with years of experience with TBIs. He offered that none of his patients attained 100% recovery. 90-95% was more accurate. That gave me hope that even if I can't be 100% healed, I will do whatever I can to attain that 95% healing. My goal was to be content and serve the greater good of humanity.

Another resource that really made a profound effect on me was Brainline.org which is an online resource directory for information about brain injuries and PTSD. They promote articles by survivors, caregivers, and professionals that validate who I am, where I am, and what happened to me.

It might sound a bit odd but the community I started on Facebook and the magazine have been very nurturing aspects of my recovery. One of the true joys I've experienced is connecting with a lot of the contributing writers over the years on social media. By contributing to the magazine, many have their own personal journeys made more meaningful. As the adage goes, the rising tide lifts all boats.

One of my favorite prayers is from St. Francis which says "it is in giving that we receive." I try to give back without expectation - just doing it for the sake of doing the right thing. I've been richly blessed. I could talk about a bad day today and sometimes people will wonder how I'm still standing but I also realize that bad days always pass and I try to have that mindset. The bad day that I'm having today can be something that can be used to help somebody tomorrow.

My greatest triumph is that I can walk through my life as a member of a shared human family. I have something meaningful to contribute. We must share our experiences to know we're not alone because suicide among TBI/PTSD survivors is real. I saw the pain in my wife's eyes and it crushed me so I entertained suicidal thoughts. Sure, she would grieve but I would eventually become a faded memory. I simply wanted to ease her pain, now.

Fortunately, God stayed my hand, and now, my wife and I are contributing greatly to the support of others who have lived a similar experience and may be asking if it's worth the painful journey.

My best advice would be to find a peer-based support group. Be mindful of your care needs and what's right for you or your loved one if you are a caregiver.

Expect that life will be different. Learn to deal with it the best you can and get into a peer support group. There will be glorious days and days that suck the life out of you. But, it is a life that can be so rewarding! You'll find joy in those days, too.

My wife and I loved to attend music concerts where there were lots of people. Now, you'll more likely find us at a horticulture garden where it's peaceful and quiet. We discovered kayaking and canoeing. I do a lot of gardening.

When bad days come, and they will; just know that this too shall pass. Suicide is not the answer. Giving up is not the answer. Even if people you love walk out on you, there's hope. You may have to continue with therapy as I have and that's okay. It's great to take stock of where I am now and acknowledge I'm a pretty happy guy!

I continue to reach for mindfulness as a way of life. I ride my bicycle more gently as I'm in the 60s+ group (understanding that not every TBI survivor can exercise). Miracles do happen!

"There will be glorious days and days that suck the life out of you. But, it is a life that can be so rewarding! You'll find joy in those days, too."

David A. Grant
New Hampshire

Resources
that helped David

The TBI Guide with Dr. Glen Johnson: https://tbiguide.com

Brainline.org (online resource directory): https://www.brainline.org/

Brain Injury Association of New Hampshire: https://bianh.org/

Important Self-Care Routines:

- Know that healing takes a long time and not to be in a hurry.

- Knowing that you'll never be 100% back to normal but life can be rewarding.

- Journaling.

- Exercising for those who are able. (David began bicycling a few months after his injury which helped with his recovery).

- Trying new things no matter how long it takes you.

- Gardening.

- Being outdoors.

- Brain Injury Hope Network:
  http://tbihopeandinspiration.com/

- Social Community for BIHN:
  https://www.facebook.com/braininjuryhope
  network

- David's Brainline Blog:
  https://www.brainline.org/blog/getting-back-
  bike

- David's Book:
  http://metamorphosisbook.com/

About David A. Grant

David A. Grant is a brain injury advocate based out of southern New Hampshire and the publisher of HOPE Magazine. In 2013, David founded the Brain Injury Hope Network, one of the world's largest online social communities that supports those affected by brain injury.

David is also a regular contributing writer to Brainline.org, a PBS-sponsored website. When David is not advocating, he can be found on his bicycle exploring southern New Hampshire.

Chapter 11

Beyond Survival

Darcy L. Keith

The stretch of road from Muncie, Indiana, to Morehead, Kentucky, is only 280 miles long - a drive normally lasting less than six hours. When in 1991, I started out on that road as an ambitious college senior, little did I know that my life and dreams for the future would come to a screeching halt in a matter of hours, not to mention that two of my closest friends would be dead.

Everything physically, mentally, emotionally, and financially that I had accomplished in my short life thus far was gone forever. Or was it?

In early September of my senior year, four sorority sisters and I were asked by our national sorority to help start a new chapter at Morehead State University. Currently serving as rush chairman,

I happily agreed. But after we completed the rush parties and were returning to Ball State University that evening, something went terribly wrong. As we entered the southern outskirts of Cincinnati, our driver lost control of our vehicle in the wind shear caused by two passing semis. The car spun, and we ended up sideways in the middle of the northbound lanes of the highway, trapped in the path of an approaching semi-tractor trailer. The resulting impact was so great that our car's crumpled side panel bore the imprint of the semi's front license plate.

When the screeching and grinding came to a halt, the two girls buckled in the front seats were able to exit the car and walk away. The three unbuckled girls in the back, including myself, weren't so lucky. Two were killed instantly. The paramedics could not tell at first whether I had survived the crash because they couldn't find my pulse; they had to remove some of my nail polish to be sure. If I were dead, the color under my fingernails would have been blue. It was pink. Barely breathing and placed on life support, I was rushed by a Life Flight helicopter to the University of Cincinnati Hospital and admitted to the surgical critical-care unit.

The injuries I sustained were massive. Unconscious, I remained in a coma for six days with frontal lobe and left-brain injuries that paralyzed my body's right side. The doctors told my parents that the prognosis was grim. Damage to the left side of my brain resulted in a significant loss of memory, and also impaired my motor skills. Brain bruising, bleeding, and swelling in my frontal lobe caused brain cells to die, which left a gaping hole. Damage was done, but the extent was still unknown.

Awaking from my coma, I was scared and confused. With no control over my bodily functions, I endured the humiliation of adult diapers. Due to the right extremity paralysis, getting around required the use of a wheelchair. Also paralyzed was my right vocal cord, which initially left me unable to speak. My right lung collapsed, and I also experienced foot drop. Eating was very difficult as well since I was unable to swallow. A feeding tube that went up my nose and down my throat to my stomach nourished me daily. When I was finally able to feed myself, I was put in a special feeding group to learn how to swallow again. Once I mastered the swallowing process, I graduated to eating "normal" everyday food items.

It was during a session with all my therapists present that I learned of the car crash and the deaths of my two sorority sisters. As I sat in shock and disbelief upon hearing the news, the therapists watched closely to see my reaction. I could only utter the words, "Why didn't I die?" No one replied except my mother, but to this day, I can't recall what she said to me. I couldn't believe that they were dead, but the scars on my body told me that something terrible had happened.

At first, my only thought was about how to survive my injuries. Beside my hospital bed was a chart listing various tasks that I would have to complete independently before I could be discharged. I refused to dwell on my injuries or give up hope. Completing each task became my new goal. With determination, I began relearning simple skills like brushing my teeth, dressing myself, tying my shoes, and going to the bathroom. I progressed to more complex skills like eating, walking, and behaving normally for someone my age. Occupational and speech therapy helped get my brain back on track cognitively. During physical therapy, when placed upright, I was like a bobblehead doll from lack of neck and trunk support. When I started getting some feeling back from the paralysis, the pain was so intense that I whimpered continuously. This feeling was like pins and needles constantly poking me in my arm and leg. But despite the excruciating pain, I learned how to stand and walk without falling over from my balance issues. Slowly, one by one, each item on my bedside chart was completed and checked off.

Emotionally though, I was still struggling. Having a brain injury is similar to having attention deficit disorder (ADD). I didn't have the attention span to focus on the information I wanted to remember. I couldn't concentrate enough to remember it or recall what I just did. Damage to my brain's left lobe left me with memory loss of my entire college major. When one of my college textbooks was placed on the table in front of me at the hospital, I just looked at it with a blank stare. No longer could I perform the required math tasks needed for my actuarial-science college major. In fact, I couldn't remember anything related to the subject.

Before the crash, I was going to be walking on stage draped in a bright red cap and gown, ready to receive my diploma. Now, with college graduation just six months away, this was no longer an option for me.

How was I going to provide for myself financially if I couldn't graduate from college and get a job? My self-esteem and self-confidence plummeted. *It took all the strength I had not to fall apart.*

Extremely upset and emotional, I searched for what options were available for my "new normal" status. Not only would I learn how to survive - I would thrive. I had all my life to live, and I was not about to throw it away after being given a second chance. I wasn't about to feel sorry for myself. Developing a memorable recipe for overcoming adversity and dealing with change, I began on a mission to rebuild my life. Working out consisted of brisk, long walks and light strength training. To mend and re-engage my brain, I re-enrolled in college under a new major, and graduated a short year and a half later, as determined as ever. The company with whom I had interned offered me a job in a different capacity.

Holding my head up high, I continued to grow and flourish with determination and a positive attitude. To turn a devastating situation into a positive one, I went on a mission to help others live better lives by sharing my formula of overcoming adversity and making good decisions. I did this by serving as a professional keynote speaker for various organizations, associations, and corporations.

By retelling the story and the vital lessons learned from this tragedy, I have been blessed with the opportunity to not only help countless individuals and organizations overcome adversity and successfully deal with change, but also keep my friends' memories alive. Several NFL teams have invited me to annually present the "Traffic Education and Decision Making" module of the NFL Rookie Success Program to their new rookie class. My story and subsequent consequences of making a poor decision are "incredibly powerful" to the rookies, as I was their age when I made that tragic and life-altering choice.

I choose to live each day to the fullest. I don't dwell on things I can't control, nor do I take a "victim" attitude. Despite the obstacles ahead, I choose to embrace them with perseverance and fortitude. I don't allow my ego to get the best of me but ask for help when it was needed. All of these elements helped me become the professional speaker, author, leader, and advocate that I am today.

The stretch of road from Muncie, Indiana, to Morehead, Kentucky, is only 280 miles long—a drive normally lasting less than six hours. But while everything did come to a screeching halt for a time, my life was far from being over. In fact, it had just begun.

"To turn a devastating situation into a positive one, I went on a mission to help others live better lives by sharing my formula of overcoming adversity and making good decisions."

Darcy Keith
Indiana

About Darcy Keith

Darcy Keith is a national award-winning keynote speaker for seminars, conferences, and meetings for corporations, non-profits, and associations, as well as for the Indianapolis Colts and Baltimore Ravens rookies as part of the NFL's Rookie Success Program. She has appeared on various television and radio venues around the country, including ABC, CBS, and FOX, with folks such as ABC news reporter Bob Woodruff.

Today, Darcy is a professional speaker, career woman, author, advocate, and leader. She sits on the Brain Injury Advisory Council for the Brain Injury Association of America, as well as serves the brain injury community in many other capacities.

Darcy is a contributing author to five books and has published numerous articles, along with several CDs and DVDs. She resides with husband and daughter in Fishers, Indiana.

Chapter 12

Still Climbing and (Re)Learning to Enjoy the View

Grace W. Bureau Elsner

"Lose the baseball cap and sunglasses, right now!" Thus was the cold but insightful introduction to learning that I had a traumatic brain injury (TBI) – and learning that I wasn't managing it well.

Six weeks earlier I had been in a garden-variety (if there is such a thing), low-speed auto accident in which I was struck from behind. Other than some headaches and neck soreness, I didn't realize at that time how significantly my body and brain had been affected. With the gradual onset of more serious symptoms, including brain fog, severe headaches, nausea, exhaustion, and increasing difficulty performing daily tasks and work, I knew something wasn't right. I just couldn't seem to convince anyone else that something was incredibly wrong.

When it got to the point that I couldn't bear direct sunlight without two pairs of sunglasses and I could barely make it through the workday, I finally trusted my own judgment and aggressively sought answers. Through the great kindness of a colleague who contacted a neurologist friend on my behalf, I got those answers. And, oh, they were difficult to hear, including the fact that I had to give up the baseball cap and sunglasses that shielded me from the painful assault of fluorescent lights.

I did, in fact, have a traumatic brain injury, my neck was really out of whack, and – the most unexpected for me – the functioning of my eyes and brain had been immensely impacted. I was blessed that my TBI wasn't life-threatening. Without a doubt, however, it was and continues to be life-changing.

Driving with such significant eyesight issues was nearly out of the question. Life quickly devolved into a continual logistics puzzle to arrange transportation to medical appointments, a sea of insurance wrangling, and struggle to maintain my consulting practice of over 20 years. As the TBI effects took greater hold, it became very difficult to read, and screen time (computer, television) became intolerable. My husband and one of my sisters took turns reading my work and emails to me and transcribed my work as I dictated it from my office floor, where I was often rolled into a ball from the shooting pain of the headaches and light sensitivity. Simple daily tasks brought new challenges, such as trying to focus my thoughts, generate and follow a to-do list, or pour water directly into a glass without overshooting it. Simple pleasures, such as reading a newspaper, listening to the back-and-forth of lively conversations, or watching a movie with my husband, were out of reach.

Through the kindness and expertise of physical and occupational therapists, vision therapy and cranial sacral providers, fascial counter-strain specialists, and my acupuncturist, I started the long climb back to increased functionality. Retraining the body and brain takes a great deal of time and patience, and I was not always a *patient* patient. I am forever indebted to my husband, family, friends, colleagues, and church family who shuttled me back and forth to countless appointments, helped me do meaningful work, tolerated my temper, sat with my tears, loved me when I was unlovable, and steadfastly cheered me onward. Although I've made good progress, I'm still unlovable some days – and I'm still profoundly grateful for their compassion, prayers, and caring!

As with all of life, time and distance are helping me to shift my focus to the blessings and learnings of this journey. So, what have I learned? Here are some of the aha's that I've discovered thus far and humbly share in the hope of helping others, especially those who are earlier in their TBI journeys.

The brain is still a mystery. We're all learning our way through this.

Looking back at the journey thus far, it's amazing how many modalities exist for healing the body and how little we know about how to heal the brain and the effects of TBI. As several providers have shared, "If you've seen one brain injury, you've seen *one.*" More than one specialist has also remarked, "We don't really know all of how the brain works." There are very few clear milestones for achieving progress, so it's challenging to know how far one has come and how much is yet to accomplish. I have found that the brain's tolerance can be different every day, so progress is a moving target. Much of long-term recovery consists of finding the balance, honoring the limits, and searching for the good in each day.

Just as amazing to me is the silence around the emotional impact of TBI on the patient and his/her loved ones. As an organization development and change management professional, I'm very familiar with the stages of change, which are nearly identical to the stages of grief. Even with this intellectual knowledge and years of coaching organizations through planned and unplanned change, I was wholly unprepared for the post-TBI flares of rage, pockets of deep depression, waves of hopelessness, and the pervasive, unrelenting undercurrent of guilt from my injury's effect on others' lives. TBI can really mess with one's psyche, and it has been arduous to move through the frustrations and the grief for life as it used to be, pre-TBI.

We have to model the compassion and empathy that we need from others.

It has been hard to accept how little most folks and some providers understand or *want* to understand about a TBI patient's reality. Perhaps it's because some TBI patients don't look very different from their prior selves. (If that's the case, then we are blessed.) The injury may not be readily apparent. Perhaps, too, it's because having an injured brain is frightening for both the patient and the observer, and awkward to discuss.

As with many of life's challenging situations in which we don't know what to expect or say, I found that some people just withdraw. It has taken some time but I have learned to start the conversation, share that "I have had a brain injury," briefly explain the effects, and gently help others know that it's OK to interact – that I'm still *me*. I'm also working on having compassion for those who can't or don't want to deal with the effects of a TBI. As frustrating as it is, we can't expect others to know what an injured brain feels like or remember to take TBI limitations into account. Unless others have had a TBI, they can't know exactly what we need or how we feel. We need to be clear and kind in communicating our needs.

To friends and acquaintances who have distanced themselves since the TBI occurred, I've often wanted to say, "This condition isn't contagious. It's OK if you don't know what to say. I'd just like to hear from you and know that you care." To others who live with or care for others with chronic health challenges, I'm learning to stay in closer contact and remind them of how much they are loved, even when I don't know what else to say. In every case, giving and being able to receive empathy and compassion are instrumental in recovery, healing and resilience. Sharing even the smallest kindness always makes the day brighter and better.

Recovery is more important than pride. Asking for help is wisdom, not weakness.

TBI recovery teaches us about humility and humanity. I've always been almost fiercely independent, and I have been immensely, repeatedly, humbled in this journey of recovery and discovery. Early on, I resented not only the TBI but also having to ask for help and relearn key skills in the most basic of ways. My peers in vision therapy sessions were most often elementary school children, and we were all using the same kids' games to train our eyes and brains. Activities that seemed silly or beneath an adult were suddenly very challenging and frustrating. Once I realized that putting my pride aside and doing the work were my best paths to recovery, I stopped railing against reality and shifted my focus to making progress. The work was – and sometimes still is – hard but there's no substitute for putting in the effort.

There's also no substitute for accepting help in TBI recovery. This journey requires the help of others, and asking for help isn't easy, especially when it's for a task that used to be effortless. As challenging and humbling as it may be, we need to get better at *receiving*. When we open ourselves up to the support, warmth, compassion and encouragement of clinicians, friends and family (and sometimes strangers) who are willing to be in the trenches with us, we experience the light and love of humanity. The TBI experience can be very isolating. Having another kind soul alongside us, even for just a little while, softens the hard edges of recovery and reminds us that we're not alone on this journey.

Base camp has moved, and sometimes we have to repeat the climb.

I've often used the analogy of mountain climbing when thinking about goals, growth, and life. TBI recovery has brought this into focus more clearly. It took me a long time to admit that I wasn't going to get back to my original base camp, life as it used to be. Instead, I'm climbing a different route, with a different view and a somewhat unknown destination. Sometimes, I get bumped back down the mountain and need to climb the same trail that I had already completed. When my vertigo reappears with a vengeance, I know the route that I need to take again, slowly, deliberately. As incredibly discouraging as it is to repeat the work, I also know that I've conquered this before and will do so again.

Building on the wise advice of several providers, I have also learned to keep climbing towards the next summit but not venture too close to or over the edge. In TBI terms, we need to set a workable pace for our own selves, take a breather whenever we need it, and keep climbing without overdoing or causing a setback. Every day we need to assess where we are and set our climbing strategy, so we can be present, safe, and resilient for the long haul.

The journey is easier if we're flexible and curious.

The path to recovery isn't direct and surprises come in many forms. For me, vertigo can strike like lightning at any time, with little or no warning. It's now painful to sing high soprano notes. One day, over two years after the accident, I couldn't do subtraction. Weird. (It did come back.) Chocolate doesn't taste as good as it used to. As a lifelong chocolate lover, that's bizarre!

Are there pleasant surprises in the TBI journey? Absolutely. Unexpected words of encouragement, knowing smiles from other patients, and compassion from strangers have made the journey easier. Looking within, I'm more grateful for simple joys, content with small victories, thankful to work with beautiful, brilliant people, empathetic to others facing challenges, and mindful of how precious life and loved ones are each day.

It takes some digging to find the best combination of recovery resources.

The lifelong route to TBI recovery isn't linear or readily defined, and the often unapparent struggle is very real. We need to be bold in trusting our instincts, pursuing answers, and asking for help to find what we need. It's ironic that many of the resources and support for TBI are online, the last place that many TBI patients can bear to search.

We also need to have courage to make the change when a provider isn't the right fit and tenacity to keep searching for solutions. In hindsight, it took me quite some time to realize this. I lost precious time, ground, and some faith until I learned to trust my instincts and drive much-needed change.

Triumphs come in all shapes and sizes.

Traditionally, triumphs are very significant, obvious, ticker-tape parade wins. In my TBI journey, triumphs have been subtle and incremental but powerful as a sum total. Sharing the learnings of this journey has helped me realize that even the smallest wins can add up to great progress.

Keep climbing.

The long-term triumph is in being open to the new journey and its mysteries, challenges, learnings, victories, and blessings. We may be in unfamiliar territory and not know the route but it's worth the quest. I'm still climbing and (re)learning to enjoy the view, hopefully, a bit wiser and kinder with each step.

"The TBI experience can be very isolating. Having another kind soul alongside us, even for just a little while, softens the hard edges of recovery and reminds us that we're not alone on this journey."

Grace W. Bureau Elsner
Pennsylvania

Resources
that helped Grace

In addition to acupuncture and the therapies mentioned earlier in this chapter, some of the key resources I have found to be instrumental in recovery are:

Vision therapy with a formal, structured plan of care to retrain the eyes and brain from a provider who specializes in this field. For those near southcentral Pennsylvania, Vision Therapy Associates can be contacted at www.visiontherapyassociates.com

Craniosacral therapy - a gentle hands-on therapy that helps evaluate and support the body's craniosacral system. More information and provider listings are available at: www.milneinstitute.com

www.upledger.com

Fascial Counterstrain - a manual therapy technique that alleviates pain and muscle spasm by releasing trapped inflammation from the body. Additional information and a list of providers is available at:

www.counterstrain.com

The Traumatized Brain: *A Family Guide to Understanding Mood, Memory, and Behavior after Brain Injury* (Vani Rao, MBBS, MD and Sandeep Vaishnavi, MD, PhD, Johns Hopkins University Press, 2015) is an excellent book, chock full of information and tips for patients, their loved ones and caregivers.

About Grace W. Bureau Elsner

Grace W. Bureau Elsner is the founder and owner of Organization Development and Training, a strategic consulting, coaching, and change leadership firm. Elsner has over 30 years of experience in leading and managing transformative change, developing leaders, facilitating strategic communications, delivering exceptional service, and maximizing organizational performance.

Elsner designs and facilitates customized workshops, retreats, meetings, executive offsites, team building and coaching focusing on strategic planning, leadership, change management, teamwork, communications, service excellence and organizational effectiveness. She provides results-based consulting, organizational assessment, training and executive coaching for a wide range of clients, including healthcare systems, manufacturing and service-based companies, federal and state agencies, educational institutions and nonprofits. She has served as adjunct faculty for University of Maryland, Towson University, Baltimore City Community College, and has been a guest lecturer at Penn State University.

Elsner holds an M.S. in Applied Behavioral Science from John Hopkins University and a B.A. in Speech Communication from Shippensburg University. She is also a graduate of the Fellows in Change Management leadership program at Johns Hopkins University.

Elsner has served in numerous volunteer and leadership capacities for United Way of York County, American Red Cross, VNA of Hanover and Spring Grove, First United Methodist Church, Volunteers in Mission, Servants, Hanover Area Chamber of Commerce and Shippensburg University, and is a past recipient of the YWCA Hanover Women Making a Difference award.

Chapter 13

Breaking Down Barriers

Evan Scheinberg

It's funny. You don't usually remember things about most days unless something important happens. But May 30th, 2008 felt like one of those days I would remember even if it hadn't been the day of the accident that changed my life forever.

I woke up that morning with a bright smile on my face. I had just turned eight years old, and with the school year winding down, my days began to fill with after-school activities, sports, and spending time with friends. May 30 was a Friday, and I was looking forward to my last afternoon tennis lesson. Usually, we would play inside, but I knew today they would let us play on the outdoor courts, and I was super pumped. My memory of the day prior to the lesson is abbreviated: I went to school and came home on the bus, where I saw that my mom was with her friends and waited for my carpool ride to take me to the school where the lesson was held.

We began the lesson and my suspicions were confirmed: we were going to play outside, which was doubly exciting because it was a perfect Spring day. I chose to play a match against a peer from the class, and I was winning until I slipped and fell after running to the net for a volley. When I slipped, I fell facefirst onto a rusty metal rod that was attached to the net. I'm not quite sure how long it took for the paramedics to arrive, but as I sat, fully aware of the blood coming from my head, I was more scared of the future than the ongoing accident.

When the paramedics arrived, they took the proper steps to move me away from the accident scene, which entailed them using a buzzsaw to remove the end of the rod that was attached to the net. As soon as I was on the move, I heard my parents arrive, and my mother struggling with paramedics to understand what had happened. They loaded the stretcher into a helicopter and, after my mom physically pushed her way into the passenger bay to be by my side, we flew away to Baltimore (normally a 45-minute drive away) where I was offloaded to the trauma bay. I was taken in for an emergency craniotomy, which was the necessary call in order to save my life.

What I remember most about the moments leading up to the brain surgery that would change my life forever was seeing my reflection in the X-ray machine. Inside the CAT-Scan tube, I saw not only a boy with a metal rod impaled in his face but also a boy who knew he had a long road ahead of him. And when I left the hospital two weeks later, the road was right in front of me.

There was not much I could have known at the time, considering that I was eight years old. I seemed to have a pretty strong grasp of the severity from the start as well. There were countless people who contributed to my recovery and healing, but there are a few that really stand out when thinking about who fought for me to have the best possible life post-TBI.

The first key is the top-grade medical care I have received and continue to receive throughout my recovery. From the moment I was unloaded into the trauma ward at Johns Hopkins, I have been lucky enough to have been treated by some of the most well-renowned pediatric neurological specialists and surgeons. I owe them unlimited gratitude for saving my life and my vision and speeding up my recovery process with amazing care. Even in my long-term recovery, I have seen some fantastic therapists, pharmacologists, neurologists, and TBI specialists who have all provided important help and insight in aiding my residual TBI effects.

The second major factor in my recovery has been my family and friends' dedication to understanding the effects of my TBI and being there every step of the way during my recovery. I have had friends that were my age who visited me in the hospital when I still had fresh wounds and were still there as my friends when I graduated high school. Their parents provided meals and support for my parents whenever they needed it most or just needed a break.

The true heroes of my recovery are my family. From the moment I was wheeled into surgery, they have fought to provide me with every resource necessary to not only help my recovery but to help me live a normal life as well. They sat with me at every appointment, procedure, and meeting, and filled in the gaps where I needed because of my TBI difficulties, while my brother served as loyal support the entire way. And they have done all of this while balancing their own lives and emotions, often putting myself and my brother's needs far ahead of their own, for which I will always be grateful.

The most important thing I learned throughout all of the phases of my TBI recovery is that everybody in the world has their own "accident" to deal with. It may not be a TBI, but it could be anything that presents them with daily struggles. My dad, who I have always looked up to, is legally blind and works hard every day to adapt to his difficulties and maintain a normal life. In my case, learning and understanding this concept led me to work hard in my life because I knew everyone around me was as well. It also pushed me to get active within the TBI community because it has done wonders for me in understanding my own struggles as a TBI survivor. But most importantly, my TBI has shown me that I am strong and can achieve anything I want to if I put my "injured" brain to it.

In my opinion, the most triumphant part of my recovery has been my ability to use my TBI as motivation to be the best man I can be in my academic, social, and emotional endeavors. I have certainly gotten a tremendous amount of help from my support system, but I have always admired my ability to remain driven throughout my recovery despite the roadblocks that I could not and cannot control.

At every stage in my life and recovery since my TBI, I have faced many obstacles in my way of living a "normal" life. Even at a young age, I had to deal with things like managing multiple medications whenever I would sleep at a friend's house, or not being able to play outside at recess for a whole year, which always made me feel isolated and somewhat ashamed and guilty of what had happened to me. But ever since I became truly in control of my own recovery, I have strived every day to not let my TBI define me.

Although normal things like social encounters with my college roommates, keeping my desk and calendar organized, or remembering which chores are mine to do may be more difficult, I have refused to let anything stand in my way of being just like everybody else.

There were some times I felt like my TBI was always going to inhibit the things I could achieve. In high school, despite my intelligence and obvious knack for writing (more on that in a bit), I felt like I would never be able to make it through college and be successful. There were times I thought I'd never be able to make friends outside of camp because of how different I viewed myself because of my TBI recovery. But I put my head down and remained determined to be triumphant over my struggles.

With due patience, things come to those who work hard. I was accepted to all eight universities I applied to. I graduated high school and moved nine hours away from home to Charleston, South Carolina. I've built relationships with people across the world that will go on for a lifetime. I've achieved numerous academic accolades and honed my writing skills. I've laughed, I've cried, I've seen the Grand Canyon, and I once jumped off a cliff. But what I think is most triumphant, is that I can see myself as just like anybody else.

The biggest piece of advice I could give to anyone who is at any stage in their TBI recovery is to embrace their struggles and do whatever they can do to break down the barriers in front of them. For the first eight or nine years of my recovery, which coincided with my adolescence, I found myself feeling so guilty and ashamed of what had happened to me. I felt like a burden, and because I didn't know anybody who had suffered an accident similar to mine or felt the same unique effects, there was no hope for me to be labeled as anything other than "the kid with the brain injury."

However, when pushing to get specific accommodations for me in school, my family and I realized something important. By embracing your status as a TBI survivor, you can alter how people and policy view you and your needs. In my case, getting the school system to view me as a student with needs based on a physical injury that could not be subdued like students with ADHD was what really opened doors for my recovery in terms of getting the resources I needed to succeed.

By recognizing that my needs are different than others because of how unique a TBI is and seeking out the TBI survivor and support community, I have been able to locate countless resources and create a strong network of people, like the founder of the Hobblejog Foundation Susan Hahn, who have helped me further understand what it is like to live in the world with a TBI as I enter adulthood.

The main message that I wish to implore, though, is that your TBI is part of who you are. It does not have to define you, but there is always a way to spin what seems negative into motivation and a drive to live the life you want to live.

"I've laughed, I've cried, I've seen the Grand Canyon, and I once jumped off a cliff. But what I think is most triumphant, is that I can see myself as just like anybody else."

Evan Scheinberg
South Carolina

Resources
that helped Evan

Montgomery County Public Schools Case Manager & IEP Plan - Once I got to high school, my organizational difficulties as a result of the damage to my frontal lobe really began to hinder my academic achievements and abilities. I was having a lot of trouble keeping up with small assignments, specific test-taking environment needs, and a collective overall frustration with my inability to stay organized. Luckily, I was assigned a wonderful case manager who worked with my parents and I to create a structured plan with specific accommodations that helped me strive in the classroom as best as I could. As a result, my grades and test scores improved tremendously, and I was accepted into all eight colleges I applied to.

Camp Airy - Camp Airy and the environment and community provided me with unparalleled acceptance, understanding, and development as a TBI survivor and young man. When I was 10, my parents sent me to camp for the first time, and I immediately formed an unbreakable close friend group that I am still inseparable with today. At camp, the environment was so warm, welcoming, and encouraging of boys to be themselves, that I learned to be comfortable opening up and sharing my struggles as a young man recovering from a TBI. It gave me something to look forward to when

I was feeling isolated in my recovery because I knew I had a place away from the "real world" where nobody would look at me as the kid who had the accident, but as just Evan.

https://www.airylouise.org/camp-airy-for-boys

Brain Injury Association of Maryland and the HobbleJog Foundation

While I was struggling in high school, my parents became involved with the Brain Injury Association of Maryland (BIAMD) and began to network through their community to find opportunities to help everyone involved in my recovery. Through the BIAMD, we were able to access many different resources that helped us understand how to help me prepare to continue my recovery with more independence. Around this time, we were also introduced to Susan Hahn, who founded the Hobblejog Foundation and has been an inspiration to me in my recovery. Susan and Hobblejog provided me with a generous technology grant that has helped me to stay organized and strive throughout my entire college career. I could not be more grateful for Susan and the opportunities she has provided me.

https://www.biamd.org

https://www.hobblejog.org

About Evan W. Scheinberg

Evan W. Scheinberg is an upcoming graduate of the College of Charleston, where he studied English literature and writing. A native of the Washington, D.C. area, Scheinberg plans to continue his writing career through copywriting and freelance writing opportunities, while also continuing to pursue a graduate degree. His ultimate goal is to write a Great American Novel, as well as to be able to go back to his alma mater and teach literature someday.

When he is not studying or writing, Scheinberg enjoys all things sports and movie-related. He is also an avid classic rock fan and has been known to bust out a Jimmy Paige-like guitar solo every now and then. He hopes to someday be known around the world for his impactful words and triumphant stories.

Caregiver Stories

Chapter 14

A Mom's Perspective

Debra Baker Scheinberg

It was a perfect day. A warm, bright, sunny May day. It was a Friday and I had the day off from work. I got my newly-minted eight-year-old on the bus to second grade and dropped my almost five-year-old off at preschool. I hit the gym, put on a cute new spring outfit, and met my girlfriends for a decadent, mid-morning date at the movie theater. After that we went shopping and to lunch and I even snuck in a nap before it was time to pick up my preschooler. Since it wasn't my turn to drive the second-grade after-school tennis carpool, I relaxed and enjoyed the afternoon. It was indeed a perfect day.

Until it wasn't.

My husband took the phone call. Why was the tennis center calling? Did Evan forget his racquet?

Did he need something? "He hit his head," we were told, and "you need to come now."

Does he have a concussion? Will he need stitches? What's the closest hospital and do we know a good plastic surgeon?

The events that followed are the stuff of which nightmares are made. The abbreviated version is that Evan, my 8-year-old, tripped and was impaled. A rusty metal rod went thru his left eye orbit and landed in the frontal lobe of his brain. There's no other way to describe what happened. I've tried – but you can't sugarcoat an accident like Evan's.

We were whisked away by helicopter to the Johns Hopkins Hospital, where he had emergency brain and eye surgery about an hour later. We were told that he would likely lose his eye but the immediate goal was to save his life. Six hours later, we got our boy back. He was bandaged and bruised and looked like he had been through a war. Indeed, the war was just beginning.

Two weeks later, when we brought our superhero home, our lives were changed forever. But we had our beautiful and resilient son with us, a new puppy to cheer him up and keep him company while he recovered, and a future for our family that had changed on the turn of a dime.

There were two distinct phases to Evan's healing: 1) recovering physically from his injury and 2) everything else.

Our first priority after the accident and ensuing surgeries and hospital stay was to keep him healthy and safe as he healed. This wasn't easy for an active eight-year-old. We relied on our "village" in many ways – to feed us, to provide outlets for Evan to see his friends and maintain the relationships he had already formed in a few short years of life, and, as time went on and we shortened his leash, to keep eyes and ears on him when we couldn't be physically present.

We learned early on that we couldn't be shy and needed to ask for help when it was needed. Friends and family were relieved when we assigned them to tasks – it made them feel useful and helped us tremendously. This allowed us to focus on what was important – our son's health.

We also had to align ourselves with the best medical providers we could find. Our pediatrician became a valuable resource as did the attorney we hired to litigate the accident. In fact, he connected us with some incredible medical professionals that we may not have heard of otherwise.

Thankfully, we were able to get Evan through the physical part of his healing journey relatively unscathed, other than some occasional migraines and other issues that wouldn't have occurred had he not received a TBI.

His psychological and emotional healing has been and will likely always be a work in progress. He has a hefty case of PTSD and, to be honest, so do I. You cannot see what I've seen and not walk away a changed person. Evan remembers every moment of May 30, 2008, and he continues to have flashbacks when his stress level rises.

It took us many years to find a therapist and psychiatrist whom Evan trusted and who understood his needs in regard to medication. We were not aware that there are professionals who have specific expertise in TBI and understand the difference between a child with ADD and a child with attention deficit difficulties as the result of a TBI, for example. As we've always said, there's no playbook for caring for a child with a traumatic brain injury – it's a do-it-yourself manual.

In hindsight, it would have been a blessing and a curse to have the realization early on that Evan would be dealing with the aftermath of his accident well into adulthood. Regardless, we learned that as parents of a child with a TBI, we had to advocate for his health and safety every day. As hard as Evan has worked to come back from his injury, it's been up to us as parents to do everything in our power to provide him with the best possible care. Knowing that we've done all we could has helped us heal.

From the moment Evan woke up from his emergency craniotomy and eye surgery, everything he did was triumphant! When he struggled to open his left eye two days post-surgery, it was a victory. When he underwent a series of hourly spinal drainage procedures for days on end, we called him a superhero. And when he was able to walk out the front door of the Johns Hopkins Hospital twelve days after he was in a devastating accident, we had a huge celebration. Quite literally, every day since the accident has been a win – even the roughest days.

Evan lives with his TBI every single day. He takes five medications and knows that if he misses a dose, he may lose a day or a week from not feeling well. He has to work harder than most people his age to stay organized and meet deadlines. He gets sidelined with migraines that are so bad that he has to retreat into a dark room and sleep until he can function again. And he will always have a scar that goes from his left ear to his right ear, a tear duct that doesn't work and a mark under his eye.

Despite all of this, he got on with his life as soon as safety and good sense would allow. He participated in a host of (safe) athletics, rose through the ranks of his regional youth group, attended and then worked at a sleepaway camp for nine consecutive summers, led a congregation with maturity and exceptional poise during his Bar Mitzvah at age 13, graduated from an award-winning public high school, was accepted at EVERY college he applied to, and as I write this, he is reaching the end of his senior year in college as a Dean's List student.

That college, by the way, is more than 500 miles away from our home. When he was making his final college selection, we worked hard to sway him to choose a school close to home so that we could keep a watchful eye over him. We lobbied hard, until sitting at the dinner table one night, he looked his father and I straight in the eyes and said this: "How will I know if I can succeed if you don't let me go? I know I can do this."

Evan will always live with a TBI, but it doesn't define him. That's where he triumphs and that's what we're most proud of.

The advice I would give someone facing a TBI, may sound trite, but it's true...don't give in. Don't stop healing, don't stop looking for resources, and don't ever doubt your own resilience.

I've often wondered how Evan's life would have turned out if he hadn't gotten hurt. It took me years to accept the fact that my "perfect" child was given such a raw deal. I had to find my own therapist and my own peace and fourteen years later, it's still not easy.

So I follow Evan's lead. I internalize every achievement and accomplishment as though they're my own. I brag on social media, in the grocery store and to complete strangers about my amazing kid. I deal with the rough parts and celebrate the good ones. And I count my blessings. Every day.

TBI doesn't have to be a life sentence, but it is a way of life. Whether you're the victim or the caregiver, you need to surround yourself with people who have your best interests at heart and always go with your instincts. If you're not getting the help you think you need, look around. Find your people. And don't be afraid to ask them for what you need.

Your road might be longer and steeper than most, but once you realized you've survived 100 percent of your worst days, the future will always look bright.

"Find your people. And don't be afraid to ask them for what you need."

Debra Baker Scheinberg
Maryland

Resources
that helped Debra & Evan

1.   Believe In Tomorrow Children's House at Johns Hopkins (believeintomorrow.org)

I can't overstate how wonderful this organization was when we found ourselves in a different city with nothing but the clothes on our back after our child was in a terrible accident. Their kindness and hospitality was exceptional. They provided us with a clean and safe place to rest when we could, shower, eat a homemade meal, and socialize with other families also experiencing medical crises. They even had a closet full of toiletries and care items to make us feel at home. All of this was available to us for the duration of our son's hospital stay and we were only requested to pay what we were comfortable paying.

I'm certain that there are similar facilities for pediatric patients in other hospitals both for when children are unexpectedly hospitalized and when they are inpatient for long periods of time.

2.   The Kennedy Krieger Institute in Baltimore, Maryland

https://www.kennedykrieger.org/

Evan was evaluated at Kennedy Krieger just a few weeks post-injury and their guidance was very helpful as we searched for resources closer to our home.

3. The Brain Injury Association of Maryland (biamd.org)

The BIAMD provided us with a host of resources from support group opportunities to medical and educational advocacy. They made such an impact on us that my husband Jay agreed to join their Board of Directors.

4. One that's near and dear to our hearts: The HobbleJog Foundation (hobblejog.org)

Susan Hahn is an INSPIRATION to TBI survivors everywhere. Not only did her foundation provide Evan with a generous technology grant when he started college, but she has become a friend, confidant and advocate. We are all richer for having her in our lives.

About Debra Baker Scheinberg

Debra Baker Scheinberg is the mother of two "perfect" man-children...one of whom suffered a traumatic brain injury when he was eight years old. She and her husband Jay have an empty nest outside of Washington, DC in the Maryland suburbs. When she's not busy running a cardiothoracic and vascular surgery practice in a Johns Hopkins hospital in Bethesda, Maryland, she's either on her Peloton, practicing her electric guitar, or texting her sons to make sure they've had enough to eat and are getting enough rest.

Debra's proud that caring for a child with a TBI is no longer part of her biography. It will always be part of her life, but her son Evan's triumphant recovery makes it a little easier to sleep at night.

Chapter 15

Olympic Dreams and Hard Decisions

Doug Hoffman

I am not a traumatic brain injury (TBI) survivor like most others in this book. Although I experienced a mild concussion while skiing (yes, I had a helmet on), I am writing this chapter based upon my experience as a parent of two young boys who experienced severe head injuries. These occurred 25-30 years ago at a time when there were very few support groups or information available to parents to guide them and their children while they were recovering from a TBI. We also had little guidance on what problems they would encounter throughout their lives because of a TBI and how to deal with those problems.

My son Taylor was born three months before the 1980 Winter Olympics held in our hometown, Lake

Placid, New York. I was the CFO for the Lake Placid Olympic Organizing Committee and as such was involved with all aspects of the events. It was also my first learning experience regarding Traumatic Brain Injuries (TBI). At the time, we did not know this lesson would have a dramatic impact on my family one day.

One month prior to the start of the 1980 Olympics, an Italian alpine racer suffered a concussion skiing in a World Cup event in Europe. He recovered and successfully qualified for the Italian Ski Team and was deemed healthy enough to race at Lake Placid, although there was some debate among officials that he should not. Long story short, he fell during the slalom event and suffered another concussion. The young man died on the mountain that day before he could be evacuated to the hospital. This was a dark day for all of us in the Olympic movement and it etched a lesson in my mind that I would never forget. Apparently, a second concussion within a short period of time of the first has an exponential level of severity.

My wife and I were both Alpine ski racers in high school. I was an ok racer who never was and never would be great. I won a few races here and there and enjoyed it immensely. My wife was terrific and went on to college, made the college ski team, and won every race except one in her college career. Although she raced in the women's class, her times were faster than most of the men. Naturally, competition and skiing were part of the legacy that we passed on to our children.

My oldest son Torry was the first to start skiing and racing. He started at a very young age of three and continued throughout high school. One day in tenth grade he was training with the high school ski team on Whiteface Mountain. Everything was going smoothly in the morning, just a normal day of training. The coach then told the team to free ski down to the lodge for lunch. My son and his friends took off and boys, being boys, were showing off to each other as they headed down to the lodge. My son remembered from his previous trips that there was a slight hump or mogul on the way down and so he headed for it intending to jump it and show off for his friends. What he did not know was that a snow grooming machine had gone up the hill since the last time he saw the mogul and had made it even more extreme and sharper.

Back in those days, helmets were only worn during the most extreme Alpine racing events, the Downhill and sometimes the giant slalom races. Otherwise, no one wore helmets, and to do so was considered uncool. So naturally, Torry was not wearing a helmet on this fateful day.

My son Taylor, who is three years younger than Torry, also started skiing at age two or three and got into competitive Alpine skiing at an early age. Around eight or nine years old he told me and his Mom that going around the gates in Alpine racing was boring!

We live one mile from the 26-story ski jump towers and must drive by them every day we go to town. I remember one day driving the kids to school when Taylor was five, he pointed to the towers from his vantage point in the back seat and said "That looks exciting; I want to do that someday!" Our comment to him was that we were Alpine skiers and not Ski Jumpers! (Although we brought up our children with the encouragement to do whatever they wanted to, but do it well.) Well, his prophecy at age five became reality at age nine; he began ski jumping.

Fast forward to the day that Torry was headed towards that fateful mogul. Taylor was 12 and was poised that day to take his first jump off the big jump; the 90-meter ski jump tower. Up to that point he had only been on the small hills. Ski jumpers start out on small moguls, then progress up to the 10-meter jump, then the 15, 20, 30, 45 and then to the Olympic size jumps, the 90- and 120-meter jumps. The 90 meters ski jump separates the real ski jumpers from the just-for-fun mogul jumpers. (The men and women from the boys and girls!)

Ok, ok, back to Torry speeding down the mountain headed for that mogul, now literally a ski jump take off thanks to the groomer. Torry hit the lip of that mogul so fast that it sent him hurling through the air almost the length of a football field according to his friends who watched in awe. Remember, Torry is on narrow Alpine skis, not wide jumping skis. He landed perfectly, but the Alpine skis being much thinner than jumping skis just sunk into the soft snow and literally stopped Torry's forward momentum in his tracks, ejecting him from his bindings and hurling him forward head over heels, tumbling down the hill. Finally stopping, Torry's body lay listless at the bottom of the hill.

The coach came down the ski slope immediately afterward, saw Torry, and did what he could to assist Torry until the ski patrol arrived. As they put Torry into the sled to bring him down the mountain to the ski lodge, Torry regain consciousness and he began to thrash around and fight with the rescuers. I now understand that this is a typical reaction for someone with a head injury. It took the three ski patrol rescuers and the coach to get Torry in the sled and tie him down. The coach had to ride on top of Torry on the sled to keep him calmed down on the ride down the mountain on the sled.

I was at my office working that day and my receptionist came in and blurted out: "Someone just called from Whiteface Mountain and said to get your wife and go to the hospital immediately. Torry is in an ambulance on his way to the hospital." That was all they told her. You can only imagine what ran through my mind at that moment when I heard that. I immediately left work, found my wife and we both headed to the hospital only to get there before the ambulance arrived. The people at the hospital did not know anything more than we did. Talking about anxiety and emotions, they were running high.

The crew struggled with Torry all the way down the mountain and into the ski lodge to wait for the ambulance to arrive. Torry was still combative as they put him in the ambulance. The coach got in the ambulance to ride with Torry and try to keep him as calm as possible. Halfway to the hospital, the coach said that Torry suddenly sat up straight and said something to the effect of "Ok let's get back up the mountain and take another run" and then he collapsed again onto the stretcher.

The ambulance finally arrived with Torry. The Emergency room personnel took over and quickly got Torry in and sedated him. My wife and I were at least comforted with the fact that he was still alive, and recovery was possible although we were totally clueless as to what that meant or how.

As they were working on Torry in the Emergency Room, my wife remembered that Taylor was scheduled to take his first jump off the 90-meter ski jump that afternoon. She pulled me aside and asked me to go home and make sure that Taylor did not go to the ski jumps today. She could not take the added stress of worrying about Taylor while Torry was going through this. And what would we look like as parents if both of our sons ended up in the hospital the same day?

So as a good husband and parent I left my wife and Torry at the hospital and went home to find Taylor. He was not there; he was already at the ski jumps. His coach had picked him up and given him a ride to the jumps. I then put on my winter clothes and headed to the ski jumps. When I arrived, Taylor was already headed up to the top of the 90-meter ski jump tower. I told his coach about Torry's accident and that my wife Carol and I did not want Taylor to jump today. He tried to assure me that he as Taylor's coach was confident that Taylor was ready for his first jump and to pull him off might impair his confidence and have a negative impact on his ski jumping career. This was a time for a command decision, do I listen to my wife or the coach? If this kid ends up in the hospital, my wife will kill me or divorce me! Yet, I decided to let Taylor go for it, and believe me I held my breath as he went down the inrun and all through his flight and landing, which he did without an incident! I still shudder with fear as I write this. It was one of the scariest decisions I ever had to make.

Back to Torry. The emergency room stabilized Torry and prepared to transport him to another hospital. By late afternoon he was resting comfortably in an intensive care hospital bed in neighboring Saranac Lake. And so, our learning curve on TBI began, or should I say our lack of knowledge and information began to show.

Torry was not injured as badly as others in this book, but what I am about to share with you is the perspective of parents who 30 years ago had no knowledge of TBI, its effects, and how to deal with their child that has had TBI. Not only did we not know what was going on, but there were also very few if any resources provided or available to us to learn about it back then in the early 1990s.

Torry was basically conscious that night as we all sat around his hospital bed. We and even he thought he was ok. With the help of his girlfriend, he got out of his hospital bed to go for a walk in the hallway. I was shocked when he walked out the door and walked straight into the wall on the other side of the hall. Obviously, he was not ok! We immediately got him back to bed and kept him there.

He was released from the hospital three days later and we were given limited instructions on keeping him calm with low-stress activities for a while. Other than that, I don't think we got much more in directions or what to expect. Oh yes, he was required to wear a helmet once he was cleared to ski again. Not very popular at the time, but as the years went on it became more of the norm and now, we all wear helmets.

From that point on we noticed the side effects of Torry's concussion. His academics suffered for years, he had constant migraine headaches, and I believe his aggressiveness or ambition suffered too. I constantly searched at that time for information on TBI recovery and found very little until years later. By then Torry was an adult. It has now been 30 years and I think Torry would admit that he still has side effects from this injury.

Taylor continued in his ski jumping career from that day forward. Ski jumpers at that time were required to wear helmets and had for decades. Taylor on the day of Torry's injury became the youngest jumper to go off the 90-meter ski jump in Lake Placid and went on to be the youngest to go off their largest jump, the 120 Olympic large hill ski jump. He held the hill distance record for many years. He also became the youngest member of the US Ski Jumping Team at the age of 14 and trained 24/7 from the age of 12 for the Olympics.

In 1997 at the age of 18, he was ranked third or fourth in the US and was virtually assured a spot on the 1998 Olympic Team for Nagano, Japan in February 1998. The US qualifying event was to be held in January 1998. In December 1997 Taylor was training in Steamboat Springs, Colorado when he fell and landed on his face and head. He was taken to the hospital with a severe head injury and a broken nose. After several days in the hospital, they bandaged him up looking like a mummy and stuck him on a plane sending him back to us in Lake Placid. Those poor passengers on the plane must have wondered what this frightful soul was all about!

Taylor arrived home and slowly recovered like Torry's experience. Now came the most difficult decision that we had to make as parents. Do we allow Taylor to go to the US Olympic Qualifiers next month? It really was a hard decision as a parent and for a kid training 24/7 for 7 years to be so close and within the reach of his Olympic goal only to have the opportunity lost at the last minute. However, I did learn that lesson from the poor Italian kid who died during our 1980 Lake Placid Olympics and there was no way that I wanted the same fate for my son.

Taylor's ski jumping career came to a sudden end that month, but he is still here today, and we are all glad that he is! We are proud of the life and accomplishments that both Torry and Taylor have achieved despite their TBI injuries and the lack of knowledge and assistance we as parents had to support their recoveries.

By the time both of my sons were adults, I did meet a parent of another TBI child who had found a support group to help her son in his recovery. The information that I was able to get from this organization was helpful (although a little too late) and explained things that we learned along the way or through experience. I am sorry that I do not remember the name of the organization. However, I am now a member of HobbleJog's board of directors supporting their mission of helping TBI survivors recover and lead as near normal lives as possible. Their goal and mine is to reach out and help as many people as possible worldwide, so they will not have to muddle through recovery as my sons, my wife, and I did.

"HobbleJog's goal, and mine, is to reach out and help as many people as possible worldwide, so they will not have to muddle through recovery as my sons, my wife, and I did."

Doug Hoffman
New York

About Doug Hoffman

Doug Hoffman lives in Lake Placid, New York with his wife of 49 years, Carol. They are very fortunate to have three adult children and 7 grandchildren who all live nearby in Lake Placid. Doug grew up in nearby Saranac Lake and was a member of the high school ski team. After college he worked for Price Waterhouse in Hartford, Connecticut earning his CPA certificate and an MBA attending night school. He then returned to Lake Placid as the CFO of Lake Placid Olympic Organizing Committee. After the Olympics he started his CPA firm which now has four offices located throughout Northern New York with more than 30 professionals. Now semi-retired from the CPA firm, Doug works part-time virtually worldwide as a business advisor/coach giving back to the business community his experience and knowledge acquired during his career. In his spare time, he enjoys his grandchildren, collects and restores classic cars, and skis.

A Note from the President of the HobbleJog Foundation

Traumatic Brain Injury (TBI) is a leading cause of death and disability for children and young adults in the United States. Each year an estimated 1.5 million Americans sustain a TBI. TBI survivors suffer physically, emotionally, and spiritually and after the physical complications are addressed it is many times referred to as a silent and invisible suffering. Regardless of this prevalence, there is a gap between the need and the availability of post-acute resources. The brave and bold stories in this book not only provided the authors with another avenue to heal, they also provide support and hope to TBI survivors and those who care for them. The stories in this book serve as a catalyst for recovery, growth, and expansion.

As the Founder and CEO of Inspire Greatness Coaching and Consulting, LLC, I support leaders and entrepreneurs to find their greatness and create the life they desire and deserve in accordance with their purpose and passion and aligned with their heart and soul's calling. I create a safe space for leaders to be curious about who they are being and who they are becoming as they navigate various transitions and successfully cross significant life thresholds. As I have read the unique heartfelt stories in this book, I am deeply touched by the courage and tenacity of the authors and the spiritual journey that their TBI has taken them on. They have been called to share their experiences with us so that TBI survivors everywhere can find support and solace in available post-acute resources. By joining as a caring community, we can advocate for continued healing, health, and wellbeing.

You might ask why I am so intensely interested in TBI and involved in the HobbleJog Foundation. In 2013 after many years of misdiagnoses like Parkinson's, my dad died at the young age of 76 from a rare brain disease called Progressive Supranuclear Palsy (PSP). PSP results from damage to nerve cells in the brain that control thinking and body movements such as walking, balance, swallowing, speech, and eye movement. PSP also results in other comorbidities impacting one's mental, behavioral, and spiritual health. The exact cause of PSP is unknown, but research suggests that it involves a gradual deterioration of brain cells in a few specific areas in the brain, specifically the brain stem. As I now know more about TBI I am certain that my dad suffered from at least one TBI in response to the numerous concussions he experienced while playing college football at Illinois State.

I had been searching for years for a way to honor my dad's legacy and to support others suffering from a brain injury/disorder, and I have found my home at the HobbleJog Foundation as the first Board President. Our mission is to help traumatic brain injury survivors thrive and we do that by raising funds to award grants to organizations that provide post-acute resources and services to TBI survivors. I recommended a book anthology. I am a four-time bestselling author of a book chapter in anthologies, and I have experienced transformation both personally and professionally because of this opportunity. I have been able to use my voice to share my stories to impact and change the world. I was certain our book would provide authors an opportunity to use their voice to share their TBI stories and, more specifically, the post-acute resources that led to their being triumphant.

I have known Susan Hahn, Founder of HobbleJog Foundation, for over 30 years. Susan and I worked together for a psychiatric health system in Maryland. I have many pictures of my son Dante and Susan's dog Java growing up together. I strongly believe in the mission of HobbleJog and Susan's vision and leadership. Susan is a TBI survivor, and she embodies triumphant behavior. She is relentless in her pursuit of health and wellbeing, and she is an advocate for herself and others to continue to push forward and to never give up.

I am humbled and encouraged by the unique transparent stories each author has shared. They are true catalysts for hope and transformation. I especially appreciate the list of post-acute resources that supported their healing. I am hopeful that these resources will support others' journeys. No one suffering from a TBI needs to stand alone!

I wish for you to know at a deep cellular level that your TBI does not define you. I wish for you to accept and utilize the gifts your TBI has bestowed upon you so that you can impact your community and support other TBI survivors to thrive and to be triumphant in their recovery. I encourage you to be bold, courageous, curious, vulnerable, authentic, unmuted, and to continue to redefine what it means to be triumphant. Together we can cross the finish line!

Lori Raggio, MBA

About Lori Raggio

Lori Raggio, MBA, Founder and CEO of Inspire Greatness Coaching and Consulting LLC, serves as the creation catalyst, soul activist and intuitive transformation alchemist helping women leaders and entrepreneurs remove their armor, find their authentic self, and live aligned with their passion and purpose.

She is a compassionate, innovative, strategic, and results-oriented leadership coach, human capital consultant, transformational retreat leader, best-selling author, and a geographical soulmate matchmaker. Lori is powered by purpose, driven by insatiable curiosity, and guided by Source to partner with women leaders to explore who they are courageously becoming and support them to intentionally impact the world by leveraging their talents and gifts in alignment with their heart and soul.

HobbleJog™ Helps
Traumatic Brain Injury Survivors Thrive

Our goal is to assist TBI survivors with post-acute services and resources that help them overcome the challenges they face in their recovery. We accomplish our mission by providing grants on a national scale to qualified organizations that provide post-acute resources. Our grants are funded by donations derived from our annual fundraising efforts.

Post-acute care services and resources include, but are not limited to:

- Technology services to assist in the regaining of memory, focus, and goal-setting functions.

- Neuropsychological evaluation.

- Adjustment counseling services.

- Assistance locating medical care, housing, transportation, rehabilitation, and cognitive/behavior training.

- Pre-vocational training.

- Transitional home and community support.

- Recreational activities, specifically for survivors of brain injury, family members, professionals, and the community.

All these services are provided to help traumatic brain injury survivors regain their independence and productivity allowing many to return to school or the workforce.

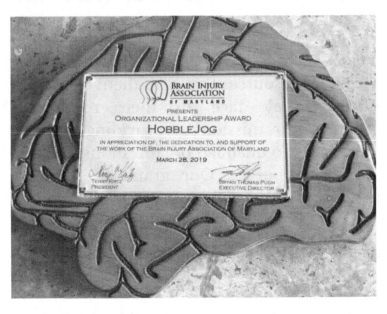

In 2019 HobbleJog Foundation received the

ORGANIZATIONAL LEADERSHIP AWARD

for the dedication, support, and work on behalf of the BRAIN INJURY ASSOCIATION OF MARYLAND

https://hobblejog.org/

GREEN HEART
LIVING
— PRESS —

The mission of Green Heart Living Press is to make the world a more loving and peaceful place - one story at a time.

Green Heart Living Press publishes inspirational books and stories of transformation and personal growth, making the world a more loving and peaceful place.

Whether you have an idea for an inspirational book and want support through the writing process – or your book is already written and you are looking for a publishing path – Green Heart Living can help you get your book out into the world.

You can meet Green Heart authors on the Green Heart Living YouTube channel and the Green Heart Living Podcast.

https://greenheartliving.com

Made in the USA
Middletown, DE
09 July 2022

68862217R00136